THE WORLD OF

Volume 4

INTELLIGENT TRANSPORTATION

THE WORLD OF 5G
(In 5 Volumes)

5G的世界 —— 万物互联
Originally published in Chinese by Guangdong Science and Technology Press Co., Ltd.
Copyright © Guangdong Science and Technology Press Co., Ltd. 2020

The World of 5G — Internet of Everything, Vol. 1
Copyright © 2022 by World Scientific Publishing Co. Pte. Ltd.

5G的世界 —— 智能制造
Originally published in Chinese by Guangdong Science and Technology Press Co., Ltd.
Copyright © Guangdong Science and Technology Press Co., Ltd. 2020

The World of 5G — Intelligent Manufacturing, Vol. 2
Copyright © 2022 by World Scientific Publishing Co. Pte. Ltd.

5G的世界 —— 智能家居
Originally published in Chinese by Guangdong Science and Technology Press Co., Ltd.
Copyright © Guangdong Science and Technology Press Co., Ltd. 2020

The World of 5G — Intelligent Home, Vol. 3
Copyright © 2022 by World Scientific Publishing Co. Pte. Ltd.

5G的世界 —— 智慧交通
Originally published in Chinese by Guangdong Science and Technology Press Co., Ltd.
Copyright © Guangdong Science and Technology Press Co., Ltd. 2020

The World of 5G — Intelligent Transportation, Vol. 4
Copyright © 2022 by World Scientific Publishing Co. Pte. Ltd.

5G的世界 —— 智慧医疗
Originally published in Chinese by Guangdong Science and Technology Press Co., Ltd.
Copyright © Guangdong Science and Technology Press Co., Ltd. 2020

The World of 5G — Intelligent Medicine, Vol. 5
Copyright © 2022 by World Scientific Publishing Co. Pte. Ltd.

THE WORLD OF 5G

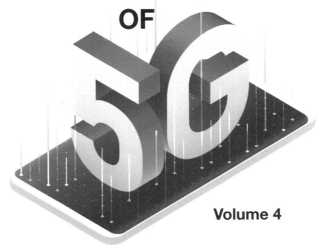

Volume 4

INTELLIGENT TRANSPORTATION

Zhiqiang Xu
Guangzhou Hantele Communication Co. Ltd, China

Translator
Lisa Ren
Zhejiang University, China

Proofreader
Lianghe Dong
Mudanjiang Normal University, China

NEW JERSEY · LONDON · SINGAPORE · BEIJING · SHANGHAI · HONG KONG · TAIPEI · CHENNAI · TOKYO

Published by

World Scientific Publishing Co. Pte. Ltd.
5 Toh Tuck Link, Singapore 596224
USA office: 27 Warren Street, Suite 401-402, Hackensack, NJ 07601
UK office: 57 Shelton Street, Covent Garden, London WC2H 9HE

Library of Congress Cataloging-in-Publication Data
Names: Xue, Quan (Telecommunications professor), editor-in-chief.
Title: The world of 5G / authors, Quan Xue, South China University of Technology, China,
　　Wenquan Che, South China University of Technology, China, Jishun Guo,
　　Joyson Intelligent Automotive Research Institute, China, Wei Wu, Skyworth Group Co., Ltd., China,
　　Zhiqiang Xu, Guangzhou Hantele Communication Co., Ltd., China, Wenhua Huang,
　　Southern Medical University, China, Haibin Lin, Affiliated Hospital of Putian University, China.
Description: Singapore ; Hackensack, NJ : World Scientific Publishing Co. Pte. Ltd, [2022] |
　　Includes bibliographical references and index. | Contents: v. 1. Internet of everything --
　　v. 2. Intelligent manufacturing -- v. 3. Intelligent home -- v. 4. Intelligent transportation --
　　v. 5. Intelligent medicine.
Identifiers: LCCN 2021061659 | ISBN 9789811250170 (set ; hardcover) | ISBN 9789811250187
　　(set ; ebook for institutions) | ISBN 9789811250194 (set ; ebook for individuals) |
　　ISBN 9789811244131 (v. 1 ; hardcover) | ISBN 9789811244148 (v. 1 ; ebook for institutions) |
　　ISBN 9789811244155 (v. 1 ; ebook for individuals) | ISBN 9789811244223 (v. 2 ; hardcover) |
　　ISBN 9789811244230 (v. 2 ; ebook for institutions) | ISBN 9789811244247 (v. 2 ; ebook for individuals) |
　　ISBN 9789811244254 (v. 3 ; hardcover) | ISBN 9789811244261 (v. 3 ; ebook for institutions) |
　　ISBN 9789811244278 (v. 3 ; ebook for individuals) | ISBN 9789811244162 (v. 4 ; hardcover) |
　　ISBN 9789811244179 (v. 4 ; ebook for institutions | ISBN 9789811244186 (v. 4 ; ebook for individuals) |
　　ISBN 9789811244193 (v. 5 ; hardcover) | ISBN 9789811244209 (v. 5 ; ebook for institutions) |
　　ISBN 9789811244216 (v. 5 ; ebook for individuals)
Subjects: LCSH: 5G mobile communication systems. | Expert systems (Computer science) | Automation.
Classification: LCC TK5103.25 .X84 2022 | DDC 621.3845/6--dc23/eng/20220224
LC record available at https://lccn.loc.gov/2021061659

British Library Cataloguing-in-Publication Data
A catalogue record for this book is available from the British Library.

Copyright © 2022 by World Scientific Publishing Co. Pte. Ltd.

All rights reserved. This book, or parts thereof, may not be reproduced in any form or by any means, electronic or mechanical, including photocopying, recording or any information storage and retrieval system now known or to be invented, without written permission from the publisher.

For photocopying of material in this volume, please pay a copying fee through the Copyright Clearance Center, Inc., 222 Rosewood Drive, Danvers, MA 01923, USA. In this case permission to photocopy is not required from the publisher.

For any available supplementary material, please visit
https://www.worldscientific.com/worldscibooks/10.1142/12479#t=suppl

Printed in Singapore

Foreword
5G Empowers the Society
for Development at a Rapid Speed

Being one of the buzzwords of the global media in recent years, 5G is very attractive because it carries great expectations from people, both in terms of the communication technology itself and the industry changes it could unleash. Recalling the development of human society, technological change is undoubtedly one of the biggest engines. Marked by the invention of the steam engine and electricity, the first two Industrial Revolutions featured mechanization and electrification, respectively. As the wheel of history rolls into the 21st century, a new round of Industrial Revolution featuring intelligence will be looming, and its impact on human civilization and economic development will be no less than that of the previous two Industrial Revolutions. But then what is pushing it? Compared with the previous two, the new Industrial Revolution is no longer pushed by a single technology but instead by the integration of multiple technologies, among which mobile communication, Internet, artificial intelligence, and biotechnology are the decisive elements.

5G, as the commanding heights of modern mobile technology, is an important engine that enables other key technologies mentioned above. Meanwhile, it can also be seen that 5G comes out when the new momentum is needed most by the Internet development. After almost linear rapid growth, the increment rate of China's Internet users is falling with the popularity rate of mobile phones almost refusing to grow. Owning to the fast pace of life, the netizens now pursue new forms of business with short periods, low investments, and quick returns. Faster speed and lower fees have mitigated the cost pressure on broadband Internet access when short videos and small programs are becoming popular. But these are still not enough to meet the requirements of the new format of the Internet. The future development of the Internet calls for new drivers and new models to solve this problem. The industrial Internet, regarded as the second half of the Internet, has just started, and its new driving forces cannot fill deficiencies of the consumer Internet driving force. At present, the Internet enters into a transition period of continuity for new drivers to replace the old ones. At a time when the consumption of the Internet needs to be intensified and the industrial Internet is starting to take off, 5G comes into being.

As the latest generation of cellular mobile communication technology, 5G is characterized by high speed, low latency, wide connectivity, and high reliability. Compared with 4G, 5G's peak rate increases by 30 times, user experience rate advances by 10 times, and spectrum efficiency accelerates by three times. Moreover, compared to 4G, 5G mobile supports high-speed rail with the speed of 500 km/h, with its wireless interface delay reduced by 90%, the connection density enhanced by 10 times, energy efficiency and traffic density improved by 100 times, enough to support the mobile Internet industry and many applications of the Internet. Compared with the previous four generations of mobile communication technologies, the most important change in 5G is the shift from individual-oriented use to industry-oriented applications, providing indispensable high-speed, massive, and low-latency connectivity for Internet of Everything needed by the new round of Industrial Revolution. Therefore, 5G is not only merely a communication technology but also an important "infrastructure".

It is well timed and also quite accountable in cultural inheritance for Guangdong Science and Technology Publishing House to take the lead in organizing the compilation and distribution of this book series and to popularize 5G knowledge in the society for improving the national scientific literacy when the whole society is talking about 5G with great expectations. Compared with the numerous books about 5G in the market, this series stands out with its own characteristics. First of all, Professor Xue Quan, the Chief Editor, who has been focusing on the research of 5G cutting-edge core technologies in recent years, is an expert in the fields of millimeter wave and terahertz. He took the lead in the compilation of this series with his team responsible for the volume, *5G Internet of*

Everything, thus aiming to well leverage the tool for the popularization of science to present 5G technology mass-orientally. In addition, with the focus on the integration and application of 5G in the vertical industry, the series comes out just in line with the close social concerns about 5G. The team included industry experts from the Guangdong Provincial Key Laboratory of Millimeter Wave and Terahertz in the South China University of Technology, Automotive Engineering Research Institute of Guangzhou Automobile Group Co., Ltd., Southern Medical University, Guangzhou Hanxin Communication Technology Co., Ltd., Skyworth Group Co., Ltd., for the corresponding volume, respectively. This book series is targeted at the current pain points of the industry, yet contributes to an unfettered imagination of the future of the 5G-enabling industry. It will be an invaluable science book for the public yearning for new technology for a new round of industrial transformation. The first issue of the book series consists of five volumes.

What's remarkable is that while the book focuses on how 5G will revolutionize the vertical industry if integrated with other technologies, it also explores the possible negative effects of technological advances on human beings. In the progress of science and technology, it is essential to stick to human nature, ethics, morality, and law. So the acceleration of the development of science and technology, with "safety valve" and "brake" being indispensable, shouldn't be based on the sacrifice of the dominance of human nature and the thinking ability of human beings. We need to think of science and technology as a "double-edged sword" and better exploit the advantages and avoid disadvantages while turning the passive reaction into an active response.

Coming in with a roar, 5G will have an immeasurable impact on the development of human society. Let's work together and march toward the future.

Wu Hequan
Member of Chinese Academy of Engineering

Foreword
5G as the Engine for Upgrading and Development of the Vertical Industries

As we all know, we are gradually entering a digital era, and many industries and technologies will progress around the data chain, in which the main effect of mobile communication technology is data transmission. Applications that require performance such as high-definition video, multi-device access, and real-time two-way interaction between multiple people are difficult to achieve without the support of high-speed communication technology. As the latest generation of cellular mobile communication technology, 5G features high speed, low delay, wide connection, and high reliability.

The year 2020 marks the first year for 5G commercial use and then the employment of 5G is expected to peak around 2035. 5G will be mainly applied in the following seven fields: smart creation, smart city, smart grid, smart office, smart security, telemedicine and health care, and commercial retail. In these seven fields, it is estimated that nearly 50% of 5G components will be applied to smart creation, while nearly 18.7% will be applied to smart city construction.

The importance of 5G is not only reflected in its great promotion of upgrading industries such as smart creation but also reflected in its direct correlation with the development of artificial intelligence. The development of artificial intelligence requires a large number of user cases and data, and the amount of data that 4G Internet of Things (IoT) can provide for learning is incomparable to that of 5G. Therefore, the development of

5G IoT plays a very important role in promoting the development of artificial intelligence. Relying on 5G can help promote the upgrading of many vertical industries. It is also for this reason that 5G's leading development has become an important engine to promote the development of national science and technology and economy and has also become the focus of competition between China and the United States in the field of science and technology.

Against this background, Guangdong Science and Technology Publishing House took the lead in organizing the compilation and distribution of the "5G World" book series, with the focus on the integrated application and empowerment of 5G in many industries, including manufacturing, medical care, transportation, home furniture, finance, education, and so on. On the one hand, it is a courageous and culturally responsible measure to popularize 5G among the public, enhancing national scientific literacy. On the other hand, this book is also an utterly precious reference for industry insiders who want to understand the trend for the development of 5G technology and industrial integration.

This book series was done under the guidance of Chief Editor, Professor Xue Quan, the Director of the Guangdong Key Laboratory of Millimeter Wave and Terahertz, South China University of Technology. As an expert in the fields of millimeter wave and terahertz technology, Professor Xue Quan will manage to make a book series of popular science with accurate and natural technical features. This book series is scheduled to be publish the first editions of five volumes, including *The World of 5G: Internet of Everything, The World of 5G: Intelligent Manufacturing, The World of 5G: Intelligent Home, The World of 5G: Intelligent Transportation,* and *The World of 5G: Intelligent Medicine.* The compilation team of this series boasts of strong support. In addition to *The World of 5G: Internet of Everything,* which was written by the technical team of Guangdong Millimeter Wave and Terahertz Key Laboratory of South China University of Technology, the other four volumes were mainly written by relevant industry experts. Among all the volumes, *The World of 5G: Intelligent Manufacturing* was written by experts from the Auto Engineering Research Institute of Guangzhou Automobile Group Co., Ltd., while *The World of 5G: Intelligent Medicine* was written by experts from Southern Medical University. *The World of 5G: Intelligent Transportation* was written by Guangzhou Hantele Communication Co., Ltd., and *The World of 5G: Intelligent Home* was written by Skyworth Group Co., Ltd. This kind of cross-industry combination writing team possesses a strong complementary and professional system for the following reasons: for one thing, technical experts can fully grasp the evolution of mobile communication technology and key technologies of 5G; for another, industry experts can accurately feel the pain points of the industry as well as analyze the advantages and challenges of the industries integrated with 5G through incise writing around the central themes to provide a valuable reference for industry peers with real and vivid cases.

Besides a vivid description of the huge changes that could be brought about by the 5G technology merged into industries, what makes this book novel and fresh is the fact that they also discuss the negative effects the rapid advance of technology may have on human beings. The rapid development of high technology should not be done at the cost of human nature, ethics, and thoughts. It is necessary to make sure that technology conforms to science and ethics with the essential "cushion" and "safety valve".

Mao Junfa
Member of Chinese Academy of Sciences

Preface

As a revolutionary leap in technology, 5G provides Internet of Everything with important technical support. Furthermore, it will bring prosperity for mobile Internet and industrial Internet and provide many industries with unprecedented opportunities, thus being expected to trigger profound changes in the whole society. What is 5G? How will 5G empower various industries and promote a new round of Industrial Revolution? The answers can be found in the series *The World of 5G*, which consists of five volumes.

The volume *The World of 5G: Internet of Everything* is edited by Xue Quan, Director of Guangdong Key Laboratory of Millimeter Wave and Terahertz, South China University of Technology, and mainly expounds the iterative development history of mobile communication technology, the characteristics and limitations of the first four generations of mobile communication technology, the technical characteristics of 5G and its possible industrial application prospects, and the development trend of mobile communication technology in the post-5G era. By reading this volume, the reader can obtain a carefully and skillfully drawn picture of the past, present, and future applications of 5G.

The volume *The World of 5G: Intelligent Manufacturing* is edited by Dr. Guo Jishun of Automotive Engineering Research Institute of Guangzhou Automobile Group Co., Ltd., and mainly introduces the development process of the Industrial Revolution, the opportunity brought about by 5G to the manufacturing industry, the upgrade of smart creation assisted by 5G, and the application of intelligent production based on 5G. Through this volume, readers can understand the opportunities for the transformation of traditional manufacturing produced by 5G+ smart creation and learn by experience what kind of revolution manufacturing innovation will create in the society.

The volume *The World of 5G: Intelligent Home* is edited by Wu Wei from Skyworth Group Co., Ltd., and mainly elaborates on the evolution of smart home, the key technologies that 5G uses to facilitate the intelligent development of home life, as well as innovative smart home products based on 5G technology. Home furnishing is closely tied to our daily life. By reading this volume, readers can understand the convenience and comfort arising from the integration of 5G and smart home. It provides a glimpse of the wonderful life that technology has created.

The volume *The World of 5G: Intelligent Transportation* is edited by Xu Zhiqiang from Guangzhou Hexin Communications Technology Co., Ltd., and mainly describes the development process of smart transportation, the key 5G technologies and architectures used in smart transportation, as well as the application examples of smart transportation based on 5G. By reading this volume, readers can be fully informed about the future development trend of smart transportation led by 5G technology.

The volume *The Word of 5G: Intelligent Medicine* is edited by Huang Wenhua and Lin Haibin from Southern Medical University, and mainly focuses on the effect of the integration of 5G and medical treatment, including the advantages of smart medicine compared with traditional medical treatment, how 5G promotes the development of smart medicine and smart medicine terminals and new medical applications integrated with 5G. Reading between the lines, readers can gain a comprehensive understanding of the huge application potential of 5G technology in the medical industry and be keenly aware of the well-being that technological progress has contributed to human health.

Finally, we specially acknowledge the funding from projects such as prior research and development projects "Key Technology of Millimeter Wave Integrated RF Front-end System Compatible with C Band (2018YFB1802000)" of the National Ministry of Science and Technology, the major science and technology project of "Research on 5G Millimeter Wave Broadband High Efficiency Chip and Phased Array System (2018B010115001)" of Guangdong Science and Technology Department, and Strategic Consulting Project of "Guangdong New Generation Information Technology Development Strategy Research (201816611292)" of Guangdong Research Institute of Chinese Academy of Engineering Development Strategy.

5G brings us technological change, industry upgrade, and social upheaval with unprecedented speed and strength, while also generating great challenges. Let's navigate our way ahead while harnessing the waves of 5G.

About the Author

Zhiqiang Xu is the Chairman of the Board, Guangzhou Hantele Communication Co. Ltd. He is a leading talent in technology entrepreneurship, "Guangdong Special Support Plan", and in Guangzhou Industry. He is also the Director of Guangzhou State-owned Assets Supervision and Administration Commission.

Contents

Foreword: 5G Empowers the Society for Development at a Rapid Speed   v

Foreword: 5G as the Engine for Upgrading and Development of the Vertical Industries   ix

Preface   xiii

About the Author   xvii

Chapter 1 Intelligent Transportation — What You Need to Know   1
  1.1 The History and Present State of Intelligent Transportation   2
    1.1.1 The development of transportation   2
    1.1.2 Understanding intelligent transportation   12
    1.1.3 The development of intelligent transportation home and abroad   15
  1.2 Quick Advancement of Intelligent Transportation under the Support of Favorable Policies   20
    1.2.1 Abstract of program of building national strength in transportation   20
    1.2.2 Abstract of the action outline for promoting the development of Big Data   22
    1.2.3 Abstract of 13th five-year plan for the development of modern integrated transportation system   22
    1.2.4 Abstract of Development Plan for Digital Transport   23

Chapter 2 Power of Intelligent Transportation Redoubled with the Support of 5G — 27

2.1 Transportation Development as the Start of Smart City — 27
    2.1.1 More comprehensive traffic information — 29
    2.1.2 Traffic information delivery in a timelier manner — 29
    2.1.3 More intelligent choice of transportation means — 30
    2.1.4 More scientific traffic management and decisions — 30
    2.1.5 More efficient transportation system — 30
2.2 Development of Intelligent Transportation with the Help of 5G — 31
    2.2.1 Difficulties of transportation solved through the new feature of 5G — 31
    2.2.2 The key technology of intelligent transportation with 5G+ — 34
    2.2.3 The best fit between intelligent transportation and 5G — 48
2.3 The Significance of the Implementation of Transportation — 50
    2.3.1 The plan for intelligent transportation — 50
    2.3.2 The framework for intelligent transportation — 52

Chapter 3 Better Life and Smart Travel with 5G+ — 57

3.1 More Convenient Travel with Informationized Service — 58
    3.1.1 Information query and planning of travels — 58
    3.1.2 Vehicle navigation and guidance of vehicle movement — 62
    3.1.3 Electronic toll collection (ETC) and non-inductive payment — 65
3.2 Safer Travels with Smart Driving — 70
    3.2.1 The classification of smart driving — 70
    3.2.2 Smart driving at present — 71
    3.2.3 Smart driving in the 5G era — 73
    3.2.4 Smart travel in the 5G era — 74
3.3 More Comfortable Travel with the New Forms of Transportation — 79
    3.3.1 Car sharing — 79
    3.3.2 In-vehicle infotainment — 82

**Chapter 4 Traffic Control with 5G+ — The More
Intellectual Management** **89**
4.1 More Effective Management: One Map of Integrated
   Information 90
   4.1.1 Road surveillance 91
   4.1.2 Traffic control 93
4.2 More Intellectual Allocation for Urban Traffic Network 98
   4.2.1 Smart bus 99
   4.2.2 Smart rail transit 101
   4.2.3 Smart stops and stations 102
4.3 Smoother Transport for Long-distance Passenger
   and Freight Service with 5G 107
   4.3.1 Smart port 108
   4.3.2 Smart airport 109
   4.3.3 Smart train/bus station 111
   4.3.4 The supervision on two types of passenger
       vehicles and vehicle for explosive terms 112
   4.3.5 Smart logistics 113
4.4 Accident Prevention and Emergency Response 115
   4.4.1 Management of transportation accidents 115
   4.4.2 Safety and emergency 117
   4.4.3 Transportation simulation 119

Bibliography 125

Index 131

Chapter 1

Intelligent Transportation — What You Need to Know

The old saying, "road leads to wealth" means the first prerequisite of evolving a city lies in its transportation condition. A developed transportation system works like an artery enabling the city to run at high speed as well as like a powerful engine of the city's economic development. Transportation plays an unparalleled role in politics, economy, military, and cultural exchanges both at home and abroad. In recent years, as China's urbanization develops at a rapid pace, it has also brought many problems, such as traffic congestion, traffic disorder, frequent traffic accidents, and traffic environmental pollution. Therefore, traffic problem has become one of the most persistent urban diseases. As new technologies such as cloud computing, Big Data, AI, Internet of Things, and the fifth generation of mobile communication are employed in transportation, the transportation system is also turning from intellectualization to intelligence. Intelligent transportation has unparalleled advantages in guaranteeing traffic safety, giving play to the role of transport infrastructure and improving the operational efficiency and management level of the transportation system. It is a general trend to vigorously develop intelligent transportation, so China has launched a series of encouraging policies and guidelines for the development of intelligent transportation. This chapter introduces the history of the development of transportation, unveiling the mystery of intelligent transportation. Some policies on the development of intelligent transportation in China over the recent years are also introduced and interpreted.

1.1 The History and Present State of Intelligent Transportation

1.1.1 *The development of transportation*

Transportation is an economic and social activity to realize the spatial displacement of people and things for production and living needs, which is also a prerequisite for commodity exchange. Transportation can be roughly divided into land transportation, sea transportation, and air transportation. A perfect transportation system consists of two parts: transport infrastructure and means of transportation. As human civilization continuously evolves and science and technology steadily renovate, revolutionary changes have taken place across the whole society by upgrading the transportation system in each era.

1.1.1.1 *Ancient transportation*

Due to the low level of productivity as early as ancient times, people often lived along rivers, depending on fishing and hunting. Fighting with nature, our ancestors observed nature to find that leaves could float on the water, which inspired them to invent the boat, thus creating waterborne transportation. *Shiben*, compiled by Liu Xiang, said that "the ancient people looked at the fallen leaves on the river which inspired their thought about boat". There is also a similar statement from *Huai Nan Tzu* that the ancient people saw wood floating on the river and recognized it as a canoe. It was also written in *Huai Nan Tzu* that Sui people held bottle gourds to cross the river and Fu Xi took a raft. It means in ancient times, Sui people held in their arms a bottle gourd as a floating device to cross the river and later Fu Xi crossed the river by raft. According to research, rafts appeared in the Neolithic Age. Ancient people made use of local resources and obtained local materials, thus various forms of rafts appeared, such as the bamboo raft on the Li River in Guilin and the sheep raft on the Yellow River in Jiuqu, as shown in Fig. 1.1. By the Shang Dynasty, China had mastered the skill of shipbuilding and learned to sail. During the Northern Song and Southern Song Dynasties, China achieved remarkable success in the shipbuilding industry. Guangzhou, Quanzhou, and Mingzhou took the lead in the shipbuilding industry around the world. Sea ships manufactured in the coastal areas of the Southern Song Dynasty generally carried loads of several hundred to 5,000 daN (one daN equals

Figure 1.1 (a) Bamboo raft on the Li River (Yangshuo) and (b) Sheepskin raft on the Yellow River (Lanzhou section).

about 55 kg), with the maximum load hitting 10,000 daN. The sea ships were equipped with watertight compartments, which increased the ship's sinking resistance as well as lateral strength and were also equipped with a compass. In the Ming Dynasty, China's ancient shipbuilding industry reached a peak. Zheng He made seven voyages to the Western Seas. It is said that the precious ship Zheng He took, which carried more than 1,000 people, was the largest and most advanced ship in the world at that time.

In ancient times, the initial water transportation system consisted of boats and ships used as means of water transportation, together with ferries set up in the riverway as transportation infrastructure. Artificial canals were also built to extend the reach of shipping. The opening of the canal was of great significance to the military, economic, and political activities at that time.

Ancient Han Gou Canal, the earliest channel in China, was built in 486 BC. During the Spring and Autumn Period and the Warring States Period, the King of Wu Fu Chai launched a northern expedition against Qi, intending to dominate the Central Plains after he conquered the states of Chu and Yue. As the saying goes, "food and forage go first before the troops move", but it was very difficult to transport food and forage by land transportation. Therefore, the state of Wu took advantage of the dense network of lakes along the Huai River and excavated part of the lake, connecting the Yangtze River with the Huai River. The excavation of Ancient

Han Canal was of great significance. In addition to playing an important role in military activities, it also played a great role in the political, economic, and cultural exchanges between the North and the South, thus giving birth to two flourishing historical and cultural cities: Huai'an and Yangzhou.

With regard to land transportation, the most primitive means of transportation is on foot. Later, humans domesticated animals to replace our feet for conveyance. As productivity improved, our ancestors learned to build vehicles. It is said that about 5,000 years ago, the Yellow Emperor Xuanyuan was able to build vehicles. According to research, the vehicles made by The Yellow Emperor were relatively simple with a rough structure. They were mainly pushed and pulled by human forces, still very laborious in carrying goods. In 2250 BC, Xi Zhong built chariots. The chariots he made were wooden carts pulled by horses. In *Guan Zi*, the chariots made by Xi Zhong were highly appraised, "for the chariots made by Xi Zhong, the radius is curved and straight, and the rope is hooked according to the rules, so the machine can be rotated and used firmly, and the product is strong", as shown in Fig. 1.2. It can be seen that the chariot made by Xi Zhong had a certain level of technology and

Figure 1.2 Xi Zhong building a chariot.

substantial innovation. By the Shang Dynasty, the use of chariots was very common, and at that time it was possible to make fairly beautiful chariots with two wheels. In the Spring and Autumn Period and the Warring States Period, chariot warfare prevailed with the number of chariots becoming a symbol of a country's strength. Talking about the military power of a country often signifies how many chariots the country owns, such as a country of 1,000 chariots and a nation of 10,000 chariots.

To increase the speed and load of vehicles, it is necessary to build roads. In 221 BC, the First Emperor of Qin unified the six states and promulgated the decree of "vehicles with the same rail", which stipulated that the uniform width of vehicle rail was six feet (about 0.33 m). The distance between the two wheels was the rail, and the width of the ruts was the same if the two wheels were the same. It was the first time to standardize the road, which dramatically improved the transport efficiency of the army and caravan, as shown in Figs. 1.3 and 1.4. In the 27th year of the First Emperor of Qin (220 BC), he ordered the construction of a nationwide land transportation network in a large-scale way with Xianyang as the center and radiating all directions in the country.

Figure 1.3   Qinling No. 1 bronze chariots and horse.

6 The World of 5G: Intelligent Transportation

Figure 1.4   Qinhuang Ancient Post Road in Jingxing County, West of Shijiazhuang, Hebei Province.

During the Yuan and Ming Dynasties, the Yuan Dynasty in particular, the Emperor ruled over a vast area, built a national overland courier network with Beijing as the center, and set up many courier stations, which constituted the ancient courier system. It was recorded in *The History of The Yuan Dynasty in Geography* that, "The Yuan Dynasty has the world around, both at home and abroad, and where there are people, there are courier stations set up to communicate with each other, just like being in their own country". It means that the Yuan Dynasty set up courier stations in all inhabited areas to help people communicate with the world, just like in its own country. It can be seen that the scale of courier roads constructed at that time was very large. It was not until the strong rise of western countries after the European Industrial Revolution and the launch of the Opium War in China that China's door was opened. Then, the automobile was introduced, which gradually led to an end to the courier station era.

1.1.1.2 *Latter-day transportation*

In 1776, James Watt, a famous British inventor, improved the steam engine by absorbing the achievements of predecessors, as shown in

Intelligent Transportation — What You Need to Know 7

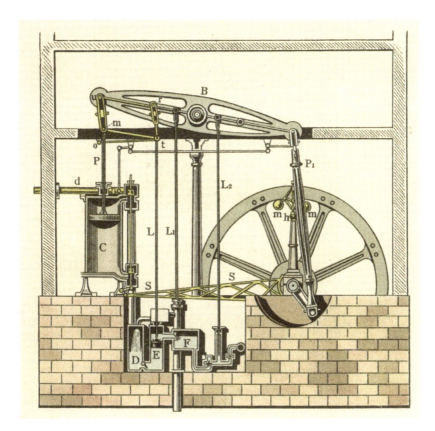

Figure 1.5   Steam engine model modified by Watt.

Fig. 1.5. In this way, the first Industrial Revolution was promoted to a new stage of development with the means of transport ushering in a historic change in the transportation industry. Being the characteristic of this change, the steam engine promoted the emergence of powerboats and locomotives, which ended the history of human power, animal power, and wind power as the main power.

In 1804, Richard Trevithick improved low-pressure steam power into high-pressure steam power on the basis of the steam engine, thus building the earliest train in the world.

However, a track fracturing accident may occur after long-term use because the track was cast in pig iron. It was the English inventor George Stevenson who really made the train work. In 1814, Stevenson built his first locomotive, the Blücher, but his trains often fractured in the tracks.

In order to solve this problem, Stevenson went to a friend's iron factory to experiment with wrought iron tracks. Finally, he succeeded and applied for a patent for the tracks.

In 1825, the world's first railway, the Stockton and Darlington Railway, was built in Britain.

The steam engine not only brought changes to land vehicles but also brought far-reaching influences to water transportation. An American inventor called Fulton built a steam-powered ship in 1803. It was successfully tested on the Seine River in France, but was destroyed by heavy winds and rain that night. Later, with Watt's support, in March 1805, Fulton invented a new and larger body of marine steam engines. Two years later, in the United States, a steam-powered ship with paddle wheels, the Claremont, was developed. It made its first voyage on the Hudson River in New York. As steamship technology continued to mature, in 1818, the Black Ball steamship company opened the New York to Liverpool regular line for the first time.

By the middle of the 19th century, as the second Industrial Revolution came, electric power gradually became a new power source, with human beings entering the "Electric Age" from the "Steam Age". In addition to the widespread use of electricity, another typical technological achievement of the second Industrial Revolution was the birth of the internal combustion engine fueled by gas and gasoline. In the 1880s, the German inventor Benz built a car powered by an internal combustion engine. Later, ships and planes powered by internal combustion engines were also introduced. The application of electric power and internal combustion engine has brought tremendous changes to human society, leading human transportation to a new era.

1.1.1.3 *Modern transportation*

Now, 1,000 miles a day is no longer a dream. Cars, trains, ships, and planes have entered the daily lives of ordinary people as indispensable means of transportation.

At the beginning of the 20th century, cars began to appear on the streets of Beijing, Shanghai, and other big cities as the means of transportation for the powerful and the rich. Since the reform and opening up, China's economy has stepped up rapidly with the car ownership increasing as well. According to *the Statistical Bulletin of the National Economic and Social Development of the People's Republic of China 2019* released by the National Bureau of Statistics, the number of civil cars in 2019 reached 261.5 million, an increase of 5,137.52 times compared to the time when new China was founded. Based on the current population of 1.4 billion, an average of 5.36 people owns a car. Cars have gradually become a necessity from a luxury.

With the development of science and technology, the vehicle has been evolving, not only to meet the traditional requirements of speed, load, comfort, and safety but also to develop toward personalized, intelligent, and driverless directions. The Advanced Driver Assistant System (ADAS) is one of the typical representatives of the intelligent development of the automobile. The ADAS using various types of sensors, including cameras, radar, infrared, laser, and ultrasonic, creates a touch and vision system for vehicles. It can be used to perceive and detect the inside and outside car environment, analyze the risk of surroundings, and help driving in critical situations so as to improve the security of driving. Common advanced driving assistance systems include Adaptive Cruise Control (ACC, Fig. 1.6), Autonomous Emergency Braking (AEB, Fig. 1.7), blind

Figure 1.6 Adaptive cruise control system.

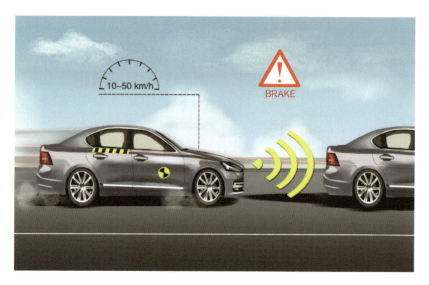

Figure 1.7 Automatic emergency braking.

spot detection system, front collision warning system, lane departure warning system, night vision system, automatic parking system, and pedestrian detection. The advanced driving assistance system is the foundation of driverless driving. In the near future, vehicles will enter the era of driverless driving.

The rapid development of the domestic economy requires the railway train technology to constantly update and reform. The research and development of the railway train in China has shown impressive success. On April 11, 2008, the first domestically produced CRH "Harmony" bullet train with a speed of 350 km/h was successfully rolled off the production line of CNR, marking China's entry into the ranks of only a few countries in the world that can manufacture mobile equipment for high-speed railways with a speed of 350 km/h.

The renewal and iteration of transportation means can better serve people's lives, and the corresponding infrastructure must be improved simultaneously. According to the Statistical Bulletin on the Development of the Transport Industry in 2018 released by the Ministry of Transport, the investment into fixed transport assets reached 3.2235 billion yuan in 2018, most of which was invested into highways, accounting for 66.19% of the total with 2.3335 billion yuan. China's highway mileage reached

4,846,500 km. The highway length is 142,600 km, ranking first in the world.

Sun Yat-sen once said, "Transportation is the mother of industry, and railway is the mother of transportation. The wealth of a country can be determined by the number of railways, and the sufferings and happiness of the local people can be measured by the distance between their house and railways". It shows that railway construction has a bearing on the national economy and people's livelihood. China attached great importance to railway construction and invested a lot. In 2018, the investment in railway fixed assets was 802.8 billion yuan, accounting for 24.90% of the investment in transportation fixed assets, as shown in Fig. 1.8. Its operating mileage has reached 131,000 km, including more than 29,000 km of high-speed rail. China's total mileage of railway is second only to the United States, but the mileage of high-speed railway ranks first in the world.

In terms of fixed investment in transportation, it is worth mentioning that in 2018, the investment reached 82.4 billion yuan in highway and waterway support systems and other construction projects, comparable to the 85.7 billion yuan spent on fixed investment in civil aviation. It can be seen that China attaches great importance to the application of intelligent technology in transportation, which will lead the rapid development of the modern transportation industry.

Over the past 40 years of reform and opening up, China's transport infrastructure has registered remarkable achievements. At present,

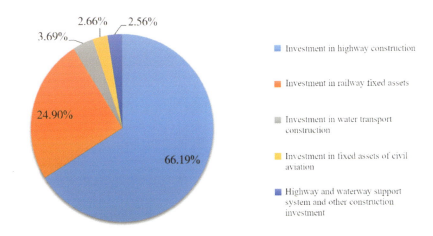

Figure 1.8   Fixed asset investment ratio of transportation in 2018.

China's infrastructure construction technology is leading the world, creating one wonder after another, such as the Qinghai–Tibet Railway, Hong Kong–Zhuhai–Macao Bridge, Beijing Daxing International Airport, and other ultra-difficult projects. These achievements are so great that China has been dubbed the "Monster of Infrastructure" both at home and abroad.

Through long-term investment and construction, now our country has formed a very large transport network. The question of how to run this network in an orderly way is worth deep thinking. The transportation network should follow the trend of the times, rely on the most advanced science and technology, and establish a more perfect traffic management system. The rise of 5G (the fifth generation of mobile communication technology), along with the popularization of the new generation of information technology represented by cloud computing, artificial intelligence, Big Data, and so on, has provided the possibility for the construction of a more efficient, more intelligent, and more humanized traffic management system.

1.1.2 Understanding intelligent transportation

1.1.2.1 Urbanization development

China's urbanization has entered a stage of rapid development after the reform and opening up. According to the National Bureau of Statistics, in 2018, 59.58% of the country's permanent residents lived in cities, while the average level of developed countries in the world was over 80%. Among them, the urbanization rate in Japan was over 90% and that in the United States was over 80%. In 2019, China's per capita GDP exceeded US$10,000 for the first time, making it the world's second largest economy. However, the urbanization level in China is still far from that of western developed countries. There is still much room for improvement in China's urbanization in the future.

The development of urbanization brings urban-associated diseases such as traffic congestion and frequent traffic accidents. Data released by the Ministry of Public Security on January 7, 2020, showed that the number of cars in China reached 260 million, increasing by 8.83% year on year. Car ownership continues to grow, but traffic accidents increase sharply too. At present, the number of traffic accident deaths in China ranks first in the world. According to the *Chinese Statistical Yearbook*, there were 244,937 traffic accidents nationwide in 2018, resulting in 63,194 deaths and 138,4.59 million yuan direct property losses.

An uncontrolled and savage increase in the number of cars in cities is bound to cause traffic jams. Urban traffic congestion management is a very complex social problem. Urban traffic construction has to consider not only the demand for traffic but also the land and capital investment and other issues. Only building roads to meet the growing demand for vehicles is simply not feasible because the rate of growth of urban road construction is often lower than that of vehicles. The construction of urban roads requires a large amount of capital investment. Moreover, the roads in the central urban areas have been built very densely with expensive urban land resources. Therefore, it is impossible to implement the plan of demolishing to build roads in many places. To solve traffic congestion, we should not only consider the contradiction between cars and roads but also involve urban planning, public transport construction, how to accurately dredge people and cars, reasonable control of the number of cars, as well as other aspects. It is a systematic project. In the process of implementing governance, it is necessary to use the latest scientific and technological means to transform from traditional management methods to intelligent and informative management.

1.1.2.2 Intellect transportation

In terms of how to manage traffic efficiently, in the early 1960s, the United States started the research of traffic control and guidance system. Then, all countries started their own intelligent transportation systems research. At first, countries had different names for the systems. It was not until the 1990s that the name was internationally unified as the Intelligent Transportation System (ITS). Various countries formulated different levels of ITS development strategic planning. In order to solve the compatibility problem of ITS in the whole country and even the whole world, the International Organization for Standardization set up TC204 (Technical Committee on Traffic Information and Control System) in 1992, which was fully responsible for the standardization work in the field of ITS. In April 2001, a plenary meeting in Hawaii unanimously adopted the decision to rename TC204 as the "Technical Committee on Intelligent Transportation Systems". By 2017, 50 countries had joined the committee.

The ITS is applied to transportation management combined with advanced information technology, communication technology, sensor technology, satellite navigation and positioning, automatic control technology, computer processing technology, and other advanced technologies. It makes the transportation infrastructure, people, and cars work together more effectively to ease traffic congestion. It improves transport efficiency, ensures traffic safety, and reduces energy consumption as a kind of real-time, accurate, and efficient integrated transport management system.

1.1.2.3 Intelligent transportation

In 2008, International Business Machines Corporation (IBM) put forward the concept of "Smart Earth", followed by the building of a smart city. A smart city includes intelligent transportation, smart security, smart energy, smart medical treatment, smart education, and other parts. Intelligent transportation, an updated version of Intellectual transportation, plays an important part in a smart city.

Up to now, there has not been an authoritative definition of intelligent transportation, and everyone has their own understanding of it. This book believes that intelligent transportation is the application of electronic information technology, sensing technology, communication technology, and other technologies in the field of transportation, but intelligent transportation mainly focuses on the informatization of various transportation applications, which is a passive management system. Intelligent transportation, on the other hand, embodies the concept of "wisdom" and tries to make transportation facilities, vehicles, or transportation services more similar to human thinking and able to make active judgments and decisions. Intelligent transportation integrates the Internet of Things, cloud computing, Big Data, artificial intelligence (AI), and other new-generation technologies into it. By a large number of data models established through in-depth data mining, it provides real-time traffic information based on real-time traffic data, emphasizing the information interaction and real-time performance among humans, vehicles, and roads.

The core of intelligent transportation lies in "smart". The ITS works like attaching a human brain to the traffic, which can make judgments and decisions based on various situations. Intelligent transportation is said to have the following characteristics:

(1) realizes the comprehensive perception based on ubiquitous and advanced traffic information infrastructure;

(2) utilizes the Internet of Things, AI, Big Data, mobile Internet, and other new technologies to highly integrate the system, emphasizing the real-time, systematic, efficient, and interactive information as well as extensive services.

(3) possesses the ability to analyze, predict, control, and think actively like human beings;

(4) adheres to the philosophy of putting people first, serving people's livelihood, guiding demand, opening up, and innovation.

1.1.3 The development of intelligent transportation home and abroad

The intellectualization of foreign transport systems began in the 1960s. By the 1990s, the United States, Japan, Europe, and other developed countries and regions had made a number of scientific research achievements. China's IST started relatively late. In the mid-1990s, China began to study the technology related to intelligent transportation. After more than 20 years of development and accumulation, great progress has been made.

1.1.3.1 *China*

China's IST started relatively late. In the late 1970s, Beijing, Shanghai, and other big cities began to do research and develop traffic signal control systems. In the 1980s, China's highways began to use the highway toll system. In the late 1980s, it started ITS basic research and development work. In the mid-1990s, foreign advanced intelligent transportation technology was introduced to carry out innovative research based on the previous research work. In 1999, the National Intelligent Transport Systems Center of Engineering and Technology (ITSC) was formally established by the Highway Science Research Institute of the Ministry of Transport, and the central laboratory was established as the planning institution for the development of ITS in China. Standard is the guarantee of compatibility and the foundation of implementing the ITS project. In 1998, under the guidance of the State Administration of Quality and Technical Supervision, the Ministry of Communications formally established the Chinese Secretariat of ISO/TC204 to participate in ITS standardization activities on behalf of China. In 1999, the Ministry of Science and Technology decided to add ITS to the national "Ninth Five-year" science and technology research project to carry out research on the framework of China's IST. From 2001 to 2005, the project of "Key Technology Research and Demonstration Project of Intelligent Transportation System" was carried out according to the national Tenth Five-year Plan. From 2011 to 2014, the theme project called "Research on Key Technologies of Intelligent Vehicle Road Collaboration" of "863" was carried out.

Generally speaking, before 2000, China's IST was at the level of framework and standard research. There were few demonstrations or construction projects, which can be regarded as the initial stage of China's IST. After 2000, since the Tenth Five-year Plan, China's government has given strong support to the policy and economy, so the intelligent transportation industry has achieved considerable development, which can be regarded as the construction period of intelligent transportation. In 2008, IBM put forward the concept of "smart earth". As an important part of a smart city, the concept of intelligent transportation was put forward for the first time and attracted great attention in China. In 2012, China established the Working Leading Group of Smart City Construction, which started the prelude of intelligent transportation construction. The transportation system thus has taken a milestone step from intelligent to smart development.

1.1.3.2 *The United States*

The research on intellectualization of the transportation system in the United States began in the late 1960s, when it was called the Electronic Route Guidance System (ERGS). In the mid-1980, the United States across the country implemented the intelligent vehicle and road system, Intelligent Vehicle Highway System (IVHS) research. During the research process, the study found that this was not only the problem of vehicle and road but also the means of transport and transport infrastructure of the intelligent traffic system. So, the name of the project was changed into "the Intelligent Transportation system". The Intelligent Transportation Society of America (ITS America) was founded in 1991. The association was a nonprofit organization aimed to help accelerate the development of the ITS in the United States. ITS members include government agencies, private companies, academic organizations, and ITS international members.

In 1993, the United States officially began the National Architecture for ITS program. In January 1997, the first version of the National ITS architecture was published, and in September 1998, the revised second version of the National ITS architecture was published.

In March 1995, the U.S. Department of Transportation formally published the National ITS Program Plan, which clearly defined 7 major areas (basic systems) and 29 user service functions (subsystems) of the ITS, as shown in Fig. 1.9.

In 2014, the U.S. Department of Transportation and the Intelligent Transportation Systems Joint Program Office issued the Intelligent Transportation Systems Strategic Plan of 2015–2019. The plan identifies a vision to change the way society works, defines six project categories, and describes two strategic priorities: "Making cars connected" and "Driving vehicle automation". There are also five strategic themes in the strategic plan:

(1) *Safer cars and roads*: Better anti-collision protection measures, early collision warning mechanisms, and commercial vehicle safety mechanisms should be developed based on infrastructure and collaborative safety systems.
(2) *Enhanced traffic mobility*: Management strategies and methods to improve system efficiency, such as improving traffic management,

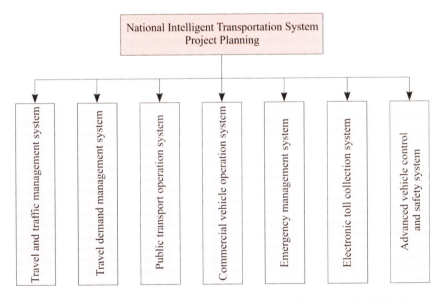

Figure 1.9 National Smart Transportation System Program Planning in the United States.

accident management, transportation management, product supply organization management, road weather management, and other systems should be explored, and the Internet of vehicles, passengers, and infrastructure should be further utilized, thus aiming to provide more information and technical support for enhancing traffic mobility.

(3) *Reducing the impacts on the environment*: By better solving the problems of traffic flow, vehicle speed, traffic congestion, and other problems and using advanced technology to guide vehicles and roads to operate more rationally, the impacts of traffic on the environment can be reduced. The plan should discuss how to provide "green" travel plans and suggestions for each trip, such as avoiding congested routes, using public transport, or rescheduling, to make the trip more fuel-efficient and environmentally friendly, reducing the impact of the trip on the environment.

(4) *Promoting technological innovation*: Technology development and innovation through ITS programs should also be promoted. They should continue to work on innovative and exploratory research topics, adapting, adopting, and deploying technology development routes to meet future transportation development needs.

(5) *Supporting the sharing of transportation system information*: Through the development of unified standards and system architecture, and the application of advanced wireless technology to enable all vehicles, infrastructure, and mobile devices to communicate in real time, we can realize information sharing.

In 2017, the Transportation Research Center (TRC) spent US$45 million to establish a Smart Mobility Advanced Research and Test Center (SMART Center) for research on driverless and vehicle networking technologies. After completion, the facility may become the world's most advanced and professional research institute for driverless and vehicle networking technologies.

1.1.3.3 *Japan*

Japan is a country with a high urban population density in the world. In order to cope with traffic congestion, Japan began to study intelligent transportation as early as the 1970s, one of the earliest countries in the world that began to study intelligent transportation. In 1973, the Comprehensive Automobile Control System (CACS), developed mainly by The Ministry of Industry and Commerce of Japan, was a set of vehicle-mounted interactive route guidance and display systems, providing drivers with road traffic congestion conditions and inducing information on the display screen. Subsequently, the electronic path induction system was successfully developed and considered to be the earliest ITS project in Japan.

In 1994, the Vehicle Road and Traffic Intelligent Society (VERTIS) was established in Japan with the participation of the Miti, Transport, Post and Telecommunications ministries, Construction ministries, and the Japan National Police Agency to promote the development and research of ITS and support ITS-related standardization activities. In 1995, the Implementation Policy of Informatization in the Field of Road, Traffic, and Vehicle was formulated. In 1996, the Comprehensive Plan of Japan's Intelligent Transportation System was formulated. In 1999, the Structure of Japan's Intelligent Transportation System was formulated, defining nine development fields and 21 standard user service projects of the Intelligent Transportation System, as shown in Fig. 1.10.

In 1998, the Vehicle Information and Communication System (VICS) was developed from Kanto via the central region to the Kansai region. By 2000, the VICS had been applied in all regions of Japan, and the Electronic Toll Collection (ETC) scheme was also implemented in the

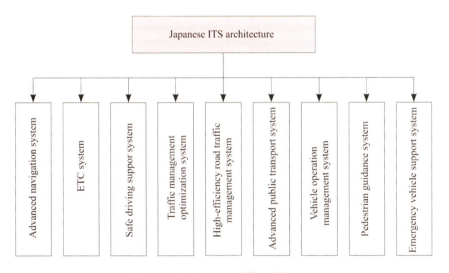

Figure 1.10   Japanese ITS architecture.

same year. In 2003, the intelligent highway combining information technology with road traffic began to appear, and the Intelligent Transportation System Manual (2006) released in 2006 promoted the construction of Japan's Intelligent Transportation System to a national strategic height. In 2017, autonomous vehicle tests were conducted on highways and remote areas to speed up the construction and improvement of Intelligent Transportation Systems. Japan plans to popularize autonomous driving technology nationwide by 2025, aiming to reduce traffic accidents through the popularization of autonomous driving and achieve the goal of zero traffic accidents by 2030.

1.2 Quick Advancement of Intelligent Transportation under the Support of Favorable Policies

In 2013, the Ministry of Transport officially added intelligent transportation into its strategic deployment and regarded intelligent transportation as a key link in "comprehensive transportation, green transportation, Intelligent Transportation and safe transportation", officially kicking off the construction of China's intelligent transportation. In recent years, our country has released a number of policies related to intelligent transportation. For example, on February 3, 2017, the State Council issued *the 13th Five-year Plan for the Development of Modern Integrated Transportation System*. On July 25, 2019, the Ministry of Transport issued the *Abstract of Development Plan for Digital Transport* on September 19, 2019, while the CPC Central Committee and the State Council issued the *Abstract of Program of Building National Strength in Transportation*. On December 9, 2019, the Ministry of Transport issued *Abstract of The Action Outline for Promoting the Development of Big Data (2020–2025)*.

1.2.1 *Abstract of program of building national strength in transportation*

In September 2019, the CPC Central Committee and the State Council issued the *Program of Building National Strength in Transportation* (hereinafter referred to as *the Outline*), calling for its completion by 2035. *The Outline* calls for scientific and technological innovation, smart leadership, enhanced research and development of cutting-edge and key technologies, and vigorous development of intelligent transportation. We are shifting from speed and scale to quality and efficiency, while simultaneously transforming from traditional factor reliance to innovation-orientated focus, thus building a safe, convenient, efficient, green, and economical modern comprehensive transportation system.

The Outline calls for the vigorous development of intelligent transportation. We will further integrate Big Data, the Internet, artificial intelligence, blockchain, supercomputing, and other new technologies with the transportation industry. We will promote the development of transportation enabled by data resources, accelerate the integrated development of transportation infrastructure networks, transportation service networks, energy networks, and information networks, and build ubiquitous and advanced transportation information infrastructure. We will build a system of integrated transportation Big Data centers, deepen the development of public transportation services and e-government, as well as push forward the application of the BeiDou navigation satellite system.

The Outline also mentions strengthening research and development of key cutting-edge technologies, aiming at new-generation information technology, AI, intelligent manufacturing, new materials, new energy, and other technologies. The research and development of powertrain systems for automobiles, civil aircraft, ships, and other equipment should be strengthened. The research and development of coordinated operation and service technology of regional comprehensive traffic networks, coordinated control technology of urban comprehensive traffic, and safety control and emergency search and rescue technology of inland river navigation based on ship and shore coordination should be strengthened. We will make a reasonable and overall arrangement on technology reserve and research development for systems such as high-speed train with 600 km/h high-speed Maglev system, 400 km/h high-speed wheel-rail passenger train system (including variable track), and low vacuum tube (tunnel).

The Outline was issued for the first time in the name of the CPC Central Committee and the State Council. It is a major strategic decision made by the CPC Central Committee based on China's national conditions, with the overall situation and the future in mind. The country has elevated the construction of intelligent transportation to an important strategic level.

1.2.2 Abstract of the action outline for promoting the development of Big Data

In December 2019, the Ministry of Transport issued the *Action Outline for Promoting the Development of Big Data (2020–2025)* (hereinafter referred to as *the Outline of Action*). The *Outline of Action* has 21 major tasks in five categories: consolidating the foundation for Big Data development, deepening sharing and opening up of Big Data, comprehensively promoting innovation and application of Big Data, strengthening security guarantee of Big Data, and improving the management system of Big Data.

The Outline for Action calls for strengthening technology research, development, and application. We will promote the research and development of digital twin technologies for various types of transportation infrastructure and vehicles, accelerate the innovation of Building Information Model (BIM) technology in various fields of transportation, and form application products with exclusive intellectual property rights. We will study and formulate the IPv6 address planning for the transportation industry and promote the R&D and application of fifth-generation mobile communication technology and satellite communications information networks in the transportation sector. We will develop and apply key technologies of Big Data under the comprehensive transportation system.

The Outline for Action requires transportation development enabled by data resources, as the breakthrough point, focuses on key procedures such as infrastructure support, share, open, innovative applications, security, and management reform in accordance with the principles of overall coordination, application-driven principle, safety control, and multi-parties participating. To provide robust support for speeding up the building of a powerful transportation country, *the Outline for Action* also requires the implementation of "big five" action to develop Big Data for comprehensive transportation and further in-depth fusion of the large data and integrated transport as well as effective construction of a comprehensive transportation system of a large data center.

1.2.3 Abstract of 13th five-year plan for the development of modern integrated transportation system

On February 3, 2017, the State Council issued the *13th Five-Year Plan for the Development of Modern Comprehensive Transportation System* (hereinafter referred to as *the Plan*). *The Plan* puts forward five goals: expansion of network coverage encryption, integration and efficiency, the quality and upgrading of transportation services, the wide application of intelligent technologies, and the improvement of green security. By 2020, a safe, convenient, efficient, and green modern comprehensive transportation system will be basically completed. Some regions and fields will be the first to basically realize the overall goal of transportation modernization.

The Plan calls for the wide application of intelligent technologies. The wireless access network covers a wide range of transportation hubs across the country. The freight business has been handled online with the proportion of online passenger ticket sales increased significantly. Major urban agglomerations will be basically interconnected by means of all-in-one transport cards, and the proportion of ETC installed and used in vehicles will be dramatically increased. The rate of preloading and utilization of BeiDou navigation satellite systems in the transportation sector has increased sharply.

The Plan calls for enhancing the intelligent level of traffic development. We will promote the intelligent transformation of the transportation industry, upgrade intelligent transportation services, and optimize transportation operation and management mechanisms. We will implement the "Internet Plus" action plan for convenient transportation and efficient logistics. We will integrate information and intelligent development into all links of the transport construction, operation, service, and supervision chain, promote the deep integration of cloud computing, Big Data, Internet of Things, mobile Internet, intelligent control, and other technologies with transport, and realize digitalization, networking, and intelligent operation of infrastructure and transport tools. We will foster and strengthen the intelligent transportation industry guided by innovation-driven development to vigorously promote innovation and industrialization in intelligent transportation and other emerging frontier fields.

1.2.4 *Abstract of Development Plan for Digital Transport*

On July 25, 2019, the Ministry of Transport issued the *Outline of the Digital Transport Development Plan* (hereinafter referred to as *the Outline*).

The Outline proposes to build a digital collection system, a networked transmission system, and an intelligent application system with "data chain" as the main line. It plans to push the process from transportation informatization to transportation digitalization, networking, and intellectualization so as to provide support for building a powerful transportation country.

The Outline calls for the promotion of the deployment and application of the fifth-generation mobile communication technology. By 2025, the industrial applications of public network systems such as the fifth-generation mobile communication technology will be initially implemented. Transportation and communications industries will be deeply integrated, and the application of new forms of business and new technologies will maintain an advanced level in the world.

The Outline calls for the layout of an all-dimensional traffic perception network at key nodes. We will promote the synchronous planning and construction of traffic perception networks and traffic infrastructure. We will deepen the application of roadside intelligent terminals such as highway ETC portal racks and build a cloud interconnection perceptional network to enable "dumb facilities" to have multidimensional monitoring, intelligent network connection, precise control, and collaborative service capabilities. We will focus on crowdsourcing, mobile signaling, and other social data integration applications. Also, we will build a basic cloud platform for the traffic control network to have vehicles, infrastructure, and traffic environment closely interconnected. Moreover, we will expedite the application of BeiDou navigation in the fields of free-flow charging, autonomous driving, vehicle–road coordination, maritime search and rescue, port automation, collection, distribution, and dispatching.

At all times and all over the world, transportation can not only affect people's lives but also affect the destiny of a country. In each era, the leapfrog development in the field of transportation is closely related to the technological innovation at that time. Scientific and technological innovation is particularly important to kick-start urbanization and solve increasingly complex transportation problems. Relying on new technologies such as Big Data, artificial intelligence, blockchain, and new-generation mobile Internet, transportation needs to be further upgraded from intelligent to smart. It is an irresistible trend to strongly develop intelligent transportation. Accordingly, China has issued a number of intelligent transportation-related policies to help and guide intelligent transportation to flourish.

"Outline for Building a Powerful Transportation Country", *"Outline of Action to Promote the Development of Comprehensive Transportation Big Data (2020–2025)"*, *"13th Five-Year Modern Comprehensive Transportation System Development Plan"*, *"Digital Transportation Development Plan Outline"*, and other related transportation policies have been launched one after another to give a strong shot for the intelligent transportation construction and development of our country. It will promote the great development of the intelligent transportation industry. Intelligent transportation requires the deep integration of Big Data, Internet, artificial intelligence, blockchain, supercomputing, and other new technologies. 5G is the bridge for the deep integration of these new technologies. It will solve the problems such as real-time mass transmission and transmission delay involved in the deep integration to promote the smooth application of intelligent transportation, turning all kinds of imagination into reality to facilitate people's lives.

Chapter 2

Power of Intelligent Transportation Redoubled with the Support of 5G

On June 6, 2019, the official release of the commercial license for 5G marked the formal beginning of the 5G commercial era in China. Under the 5G blueprint of "information arrives whenever we want, everything is within reach", people conceive broadly and freely about the 5G life in the future. With 5G's support, what will intelligent transportation in the future look like? How will 5G key technologies help the development of intelligent transportation? How will the construction of intelligent transportation be implemented? Answers to these questions will be introduced one by one in this chapter.

2.1 Transportation Development as the Start of Smart City

Vision of 5G Life

One day in 2035, at 6:30 in the morning, when you wake up, the smart terminal automatically presents the day's schedule and weather conditions to you. After reading the information, you decide to add another coat before you go out.

At 7 o' clock, you walk out of your house and open the door of the driverless car waiting on the side of the road. The vehicle is booked in advance according to the travel plan for the day. After you close the door, the car seat automatically adjusts to the optimal position and comfort level for your body based on the history of your ride. Then, according to previous listening records, the car would turn on your favorite background music, "High Mountain and Running Water" and broadcast the morning stock market commentary program of the financial host you have been following recently. By reading and analyzing the health data of the smart terminal you're wearing, the on-board system would recommend a breakfast of one cup of milk and two eggs and suggest reducing your fat intake of that day.

Before the vehicle moves, the vehicle would collect the opening and closing time of all traffic lights along the planned road to accurately calculate the vehicle speed on the precondition of safe driving and punctual arrival, thus ensuring no stopping and stable speed throughout the journey, as shown in Fig. 2.1. After five minutes of driving, the car received real-time information from the vehicle dispatch center, finding that the original driving route was congested due to a traffic accident, then automatically planning an alternate route and turning right at the next intersection in time. At this point, the car would scan the roadside store information and find that a nearby movie theater will be showing a big movie next Wednesday, which is exactly in line with your viewing preferences so it would push the movie information to your smart terminal. You browse the information and pay on the smart terminal to complete the movie-booking order.

Figure 2.1   Driverless car.

> At 7:45, the car stops smoothly and on time in front of the company building. After you get off the car and close the door, you would immediately receive the journey record issued by the system, including the time of getting on and off the car, driving route, mileage, and other information and attach the cost list of this journey. At this point, the car has automatically left the company's office area, heading toward the next reserved passenger get-on place.

The above scenes are only a fragment of our daily life in the smart city of the future that we have envisioned, rather than what most people think may be an episode of a scene from a Hollywood Sci-Fi blockbuster. In the future, combined with the construction and development of cities, urban transportation will undergo earth-shaking changes, which are specifically reflected in the following five aspects.

2.1.1 *More comprehensive traffic information*

The rapid development of the Internet of Things will realize the automatic interconnection of multiple systems such as transportation system, media system, and weather as well as vehicles, traffic poles, street lights, and pedestrian wearable devices. The sources of traffic information will be more extensive, including the types of vehicles that people choose to travel in, fuel consumption, weather, air quality, intersections, and traffic lights along the route and other related information.

2.1.2 *Traffic information delivery in a timelier manner*

With the development of information technology and the innovation of transmission technology, the delivery of traffic information becomes faster and faster. During the journey of a vehicle, in addition to automatically detecting the surroundings and responding to it in time to achieve safe driving, it can also receive traffic-related information in the environment in time, such as congestion information, the average speed of vehicles in the relevant section, the next green light in front of the traffic, and the countdown time. With this information, the vehicle can choose the proper driving mode and driving speed in time according to the road conditions to adapt to the traffic conditions under the current environment.

2.1.3 *More intelligent choice of transportation means*

Coupled with mature applications of AI and Big Data technology, a powerful intelligent traffic management platform can be more familiar with everyone's travel behavior and preferences so as to automatically form travel plans more in line with people's needs. At the same time, the platform can provide a variety of transportation modes for people to choose according to the traffic conditions around the travel transfer node. For example, when people arrive at a city for the first time, they can receive the transportation mode (such as taxi, subway, and self-driving) recommended by the system according to the current traffic conditions, the corresponding route, and the cost of time after getting off the plane, convenient for people to make their own choices and realize low-carbon travel, green life, and sustainable development.

2.1.4 *More scientific traffic management and decisions*

More comprehensive traffic information data can be obtained through the full network of traffic facilities and the complete collection of traffic information. Through in-depth analysis and modeling of traffic information data, traffic scheduling and traffic planning can be made more scientific. Traffic Big Data can be used for simulation analysis, ranging from the relief of road congestion, the optimization of traffic light signal length to the adjustment of bus route, and the construction of traffic trunk roads. Also, it can carry out real-time monitoring of traffic flow for emergencies and major celebrations to deduce changes in traffic flow, thus doing a good job in emergency control.

2.1.5 *More efficient transportation system*

With the gradual implementation of intelligent transportation and the more mature application of "5G+ Internet of Things + Big Data + AI technology", a network covering the whole journey and the whole region (land, sea, and air) will be realized. Convenient methods, such as "face swiping" as well as check-in and "scan" payment, will not only improve personal travel efficiency but also make the transportation network more intelligent. The popularization of "one-stop" public transportation and "one-system" cargo transportation will greatly improve the transportation efficiency.

2.2 Development of Intelligent Transportation with the Help of 5G

2.2.1 *Difficulties of transportation solved through the new feature of 5G*

5G is the abbreviation of the fifth-generation mobile communication technology. 3GPP (Third Generation Partnership Plan), the International Organization for Standardization, defines three scenarios for 5G: Enhanced Mobile Broadband (eMBB), Massive Machine Type Communication (mMTC), and Ultra-Reliable Low-Latency Communication (URLLC). 5G offers higher key performance indicators than 4G, supporting user experience rate of 0.1–1 Gb/s, connection density of one million per square kilometer, end-to-end delay of milliseconds, traffic density of tens of terabytes per second per square kilometer, mobility of more than 500 km per hour, and peak rate of tens of gigabytes per second. Among them, user experience rate, connection density, and delivery delay are the three most basic performance indicators of 5G, as shown in Tables 2.1 and 2.2.

Table 2.1 Definition of 5G performance indicators.

Name	Definition
User experience rate	The lowest delivery rate available to users in a real network environment
Connection density	The total number of in-line devices supported per unit area of connection density
End-to-end delay	The time at which a packet is transmitted from the source node to the destination node for proper reception
Mobility	The maximum relative moving speed between the transceiver and the receiver when certain performance requirements are met
Traffic density	The total flow per unit area
User peak rate	Maximum transmission rate available per user

Table 2.2 Comparison of 4G and 5G key indicators.

Key performance indicators	4G	5G
User peak rate	1 Gb/s	10–100 Gb/s
User experience rate	10 Mb/s	0.1–1 Gb/s
End-to-end delay	10 ms	1 ms
Connection density	$1 \times 10^5/km^2$	$1 \times 10^6/km^2$
Traffic density	0.1 Tb/(s·km^2)	10–100 Tb/(s·km^2)
Mobility	350 km/h	>500 km/h

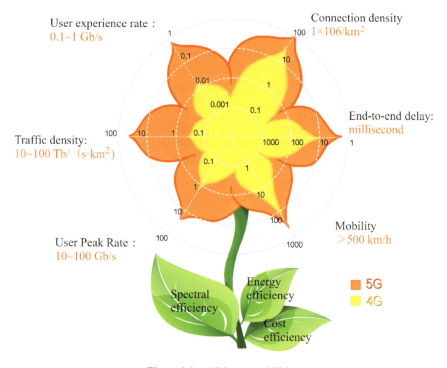

Figure 2.2 5G key capabilities.

Performance requirements and efficiency requirements together define the nine key capabilities of 5G.

The "5G Flower" proposed by China Mobile Communications Corporation, as shown in Fig. 2.2, perfectly illustrates these nine key capabilities and is accepted by the International Telecommunication

Union (ITU). The petals represent the six performance indicators of 5G, the green leaves represent the three efficiency indicators of 5G, and the apex of the petal represents the maximum value of the corresponding indicators.

As an extension of the 4G technology, 5G has made up for the shortcomings of the 4G technology, further improving system performance in terms of throughput rate, delay, number of connections, energy consumption, and other aspects. Compared with previous mobile communications, 5G is not only for "people" but also for "things". 5G is committed to industrial application and industrial upgrading in all walks of life.

4G changes life, while 5G changes the society. The arrival of 5G will influence all industries, as shown in Fig. 2.3. In the future, 5G will be used as the communication carrier and will be deeply integrated with cloud computing, Big Data, artificial intelligence, and other new-generation technologies. It will penetrate into all sectors of society and change every aspect of people's lives, particularly the field of transportation. The entire transportation industry will usher in a technological transformation. As a result, the industry will focus on quality and efficiency, not the pursuit of speed and scale. It will pay more attention to integrated development instead of relatively independent development of various transportation modes. Moreover, it will emphasize more on innovation-driven change, rather than the traditional factor drive.

Figure 2.3   Overall vision of 5G.

2.2.2 The key technology of intelligent transportation with 5G+

2.2.2.1 Edge of computing

Octopuses are regarded as one of the most intelligent animals. They are extremely agile and quick at hunting with excellent coordination in their tentacles which are never entangled into knots. This is due to their special neural structures. The octopus has about 500 million neurons, 60% of which are located in its eight tentacles and only 40% in its brain. Each tentacle has a separate neuron system and has its own thoughts. The tentacles can also communicate directly by bypassing the brain, so the brain is kept in the dark about what the tentacles are doing.

Edge computing is the octopus' tentacle, where some terminal data are processed directly in the distributed edge chips/data centers without going through the cloud (the brain). The processing center is close to the data source, so this processing greatly reduces the network bandwidth pressure and reduces the data processing response time. At the same time, some data are processed directly on the edge without cloud, which also improves the security and privacy of data.

Mobile Edge Computing (MEC) is the application of edge computing in a mobile communication network. Building a cloud service environment at the end of the Radio Access Network (RAN) and achieving the goals of saving cost, reducing delay, reducing Round Trip Time (RTT), as well as optimizing traffic can enhance physical security and improve cache efficiency by making certain network services and network functions depart from the core network. Based on MEC, end users can obtain more extreme experiences, richer applications, and more secure and reliable data.

MEC can be integrated with Internet of Vehicles, as shown in Fig. 2.4. A large amount of video information usually produced by the camera of traffic monitoring, which, if delivered to the control center, will bring great challenges to the network of the traffic control center. If most of the video data are processed locally and only important videos are accurately uploaded or when the control center issues the video query instruction, the system efficiency will be greatly improved. For this kind of data processing, MEC is an excellent choice.

In addition, in the future, automatic driving, anti-collision detection of vehicles, intersection control, lane change, and other operations require

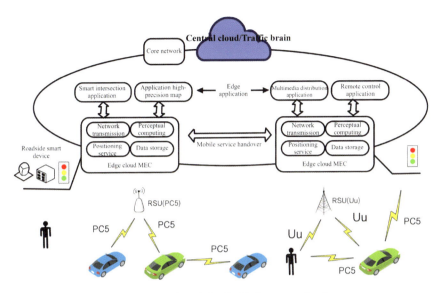

Figure 2.4   MEC and C-V2X fusion scenario view.

the vehicle control system to make the right response in a very short time after detecting abnormal environmental changes in the surroundings, which will be very strict with the delay requirements. MEC technology combined with 5G can make the delay meet the millisecond level, which can perfectly solve the delay problem existing in automatic driving.

In addition, based on the open interface of MEC, third-party application developers can make full use of the underlying information of the communication network provided by mobile operators to develop location-based precision marketing services and provide high-value intelligent services in combination with Big Data analysis. For example, indoor positioning and Internet of Vehicles can rely on the MEC open interface to analyze whether the Wi-Fi, people, vehicles, intelligent street lights, and other information around the user or the vehicle are in the same MEC network so as to achieve rapid positioning and improve user perception.

2.2.2.2 *Ultra-dense networking*

Intelligent transportation first needs to be built on ubiquitous transportation infrastructure, such as cameras and roadside units. These infrastructure communications involve the real-time transmission of massive amounts of data. In the near future, even with the L4/L5 level of autonomous driving, the amount of data transmitted between cars, cars and people, cars and infrastructure will be staggering.

In addition to meeting the capacity requirements of intelligent transportation, 5G networks also have to meet the needs of applications in other fields. In the future, the data flow will see an explosive growth, with an increase of more than 1,000 times in some hot spots. However, wireless physical layer technology (such as coding technology, modulation technology, and multiple access technology) can only improve the frequency spectrum efficiency by about 10 times. In addition, even if a wider bandwidth is adopted, it can only improve the delivery rate by dozens of times far from meeting the capacity requirements of 5G.

5G adopts ultra-dense network deployment, which can significantly improve spectrum efficiency, improve network coverage, and greatly improve system capacity by reducing cell radius and obtaining greater cell fragmentation gain. Ultra-dense networking is one of the key technologies for 5G to enhance system capacity.

5G ultra-dense networking is a heterogeneous network, which means low power transmission nodes are deployed in the macro cell coverage area to form a multi-layer heterogeneous network composed of macrocell and small cell. 5G not only has a large number of transmission nodes, but each transmission node may also work in different frequency bands (such as 2 GHz and MMW), using different types of spectrum resources (authorized and unauthorized) and adopting different wireless transmission technologies (Wi-Fi, LTE, and WCDMA). A heterogeneous network can not only ensure the coverage, improve the flexibility of cell division and system capacity, and share the business pressure of macrocell but also expand the coverage of macrocell.

With the continuous improvement of network density, interference and mobility problems become more and more serious, and the traditional base cell-centered architecture can no longer meet the requirements. Suppose you are driving a vehicle and the on-board terminal is engaged in data communication. The architecture centered on the base station community adopts the dual-connection technology introduced by LTE R12, which allows the terminal control surface to be connected to the macro station and the user surface to be connected to both the macro station and the low-power transmission node. When the small cell switch occurs in the process of vehicle driving, the data communication connection will not be interrupted. However, due to the large difference between the throughput provided by the macro station and the throughput provided by the small cell, the physical layer throughput will be greatly reduced during the switch, and the "consistent user experience" cannot be achieved. 5G brings forward the user-centered cell virtualization technology, with "user-centered" resources allocation as its core, which can achieve the goal of "consistent user experience". Virtual cell technology combines the access points around the user into a virtual cell and serves the user jointly with it as the center. As the user moves, new access points join the cell, and out-of-date access points are quickly removed. Figure 2.5 shows how a user-centered virtual cell works. Specifically, a large number of access points around the user constitute a virtual cell to ensure that the user is in the center of the virtual cell. One or more access points will be replaced by new access points, which means that as users move, new access points will join the edge of the cell. The main advantage of this virtual community is that it maintains a high user experience rate.

With the increase of cell deployment density, the ultra-dense network will face many new technical challenges, such as interference, mobility, site location, transmission resources, and deployment costs. Therefore, flexibly deploying and maintaining, managing, and suppressing interference, access and return, joint design and cell virtualization technology are important research directions of ultra-dense networking.

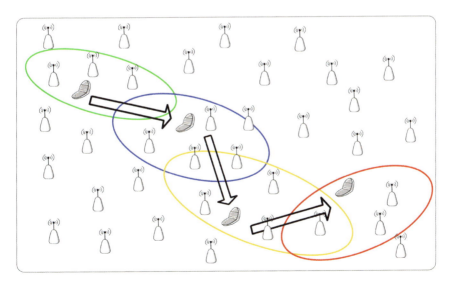

Figure 2.5 How user-centered virtual cells work.

2.2.2.3 Large-scale multi-input multi-output

Multiple-Input Multiple-Output (MIMO) technology, as its name implies, points to the transmitter and the receiver, respectively, using multiple transmit antennas and receive antennas. MIMO technology has been widely used in the 4G era, except that 4G MIMO uses up to eight antennas, while in 5G, 16/32/64/128 antennas can be used and even larger. Therefore, the 5G era is also called massive MIMO.

What is the use of large-scale MIMO? For example, during each holiday, there will be a large number of vehicles waiting in the ETC toll station on the expressway. The current ETC generally uses the DSRC technology, with its physical layer using the IEEE 802.11 a protocol standard and using the OFDM (Orthogonal Frequency-Division Multiplexing) modulation mode. It provides a higher data transfer rate and can effectively resist the multi-path interference for vehicles in a high-speed mobile environment. But on the way with vehicle density, it can also provide a limited number of channels. Large-scale MIMO technology applications have unique advantages in multi-user scenarios in key areas. If large-scale MIMO technology is adopted in the ETC system, the system capacity can be effectively increased without increasing the bandwidth of the system. Furthermore, accurate and real-time data acquisition and cost settlement can be carried out for a large number of vehicles running at high speed.

How does the large-scale MIMO work? Besides the large-scale antenna array, large-scale MIMO also adopts beamforming technology. Beamforming can be said to be the soul of large-scale MIMO, with the two complements indispensable to each other. Beamforming is a technique of adaptive adjustment of antenna array radiation pattern according to the specific scene. Simply put, traditional antennas are like light bulbs that light up a room. Beamforming, on the other hand, is like a flashlight. The light can be intelligently focused on the target and the number of flashlights can be constructed according to the number of targets. The larger the number and the scale of antennas are, the greater the role of beam plays. In the era of 5G, antenna array expands from one dimension to two dimensions, and beamforming can control the shape of antenna pattern in the horizontal direction and vertical direction at the same time, evolving into three-dimensional beamforming. Three-dimensional beamforming is like a flashlight beam following a target horizontally or vertically, ensuring the illumination of the target.

In the 5G era of high-speed mobile data rate and large channel capacity, large-scale MIMO has unique advantages, which are outlined in the following.

More accurate 3D beamforming can improve the strength of the terminal receiving signal. Different beams have their own small aggregation area with the user always in the best signal area of the cell.

At the same time, the same frequency provides services for more users, improving the network capacity. Independent narrow beam coverage in the coverage space for different users enables the antenna system to transmit data of different users at the same time, thus improving the system throughput and network capacity by dozens of times.

It can effectively reduce the interference between the cells. The narrowness of the antenna beam and the accurate coverage for the user greatly reduced the interference to the adjacent area.

It can provide better coverage of remote and proximal cells. The degree of freedom of the beam in both horizontal and vertical directions provides flexibility and performance advantages in continuous coverage to improve signal coverage for both remote edge users of the cell and near end users with the so-called "tower blackening" phenomenon under the antenna.

According to the advantages of large-scale MIMO, common typical scenarios mainly include multi-user scenarios in key areas. Large-scale antenna and accurate beam coverage can not only improve capacity but also significantly improve user experience rate. In the scene of high-rise building coverage, 3D beamforming can effectively improve the coverage capability in both horizontal and vertical directions and can cover both high and low floors at the same time. It can not only cover all users but also effectively improve the signal quality by using beamforming, as shown in Fig. 2.6.

2.2.2.4 *Network slicing*

Network slicing (NS) is an on-demand networking mode that enables operators to construct multiple virtual end-to-end networks on a unified infrastructure. Each network slice conducts logical isolation from the wireless access network, hosting network, and core network to adapt to various types of applications.

The Software-Defined Networking (SDN) and Network Functions Virtualization (NFV) are the foundation of network segmentation.

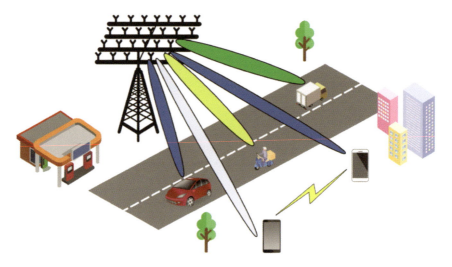

Figure 2.6   Massive MIMO.

SDN, a new network architecture, separates the control plane of network equipment from the data forwarding plane and centralizes the control function of the network on the controller so as to realize the programmability of the network. NFV technology is a technology that decouples hardware from software, integrates network functions into industry-standard servers, switches, and storage hardware, provides an optimized virtualized data plane, and replaces traditional physical network devices with software running on the server.

The 3GPP protocol is defined by three types of network section supporting the three application scenarios proposed by the ITV, which are eMBB, URLLC, and mMTC. It can avoid the huge cost of building a new independent network for each business and the problem of restricting business development. At the same time, the isolation between network slices also ensures the security of the network, as shown in Fig. 2.7. The introduction of NS makes the network more flexible, which is mainly reflected in the aspects of on-demand customization, real-time deployment, dynamic guarantee, and so on.

NS, in essence, divides the operator's physical network into multiple virtual networks, and each virtual network is divided according to different service requirements, such as mobility, billing, policy control, delay, bandwidth, security, and reliability so as to flexibly cope with different network application scenarios. For example, a large-scale Internet of

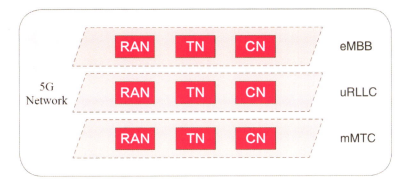

Figure 2.7 5G NS.

Things service that connects fixed sensors only to measure weather information like temperature, humidity, and rainfall does not require switching, location updates, and other features that are the main services of mobile networks. Internet of Things services with instant response, such as autonomous driving and remotely controlled robots, require end-to-end delays in milliseconds, far different from mobile broadband. NS technology can provide a good solution for such problems so that different application scenarios with vastly different business characteristics and requirements can share the same telecommunication level network with 99.99% reliability.

In the future, from the Augmented Reality (AR) and Virtual Reality (VR) which are commonly seen by people to automatic driving, intelligent transportation, and Unmanned Aerial Vehicle (UAV) and further to logistics warehousing, industrial automation, and the Internet of Everything, 5G, as a new generation of communications infrastructure, will support a large number of vertical industry diversification business scenarios (Fig. 2.8) to promote the transformation and upgrading of industries. The end-to-end NS capability of the 5G network can flexibly and dynamically allocate and release the required network resources to meet different demands in the whole network and further dynamically optimize the network connection to reduce costs and improve benefits.

2.2.2.5 End-to-end communication technology

End-to-End (D2D) Communication technology, a new technology under the control of the system, allows direct communication between terminals

42 *The World of 5G: Intelligent Transportation*

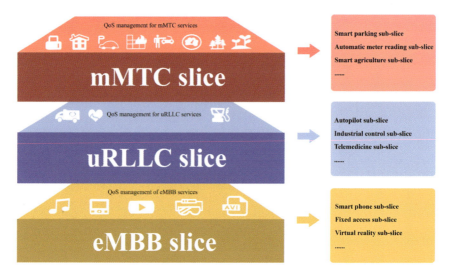

Figure 2.8 Network slicing.

through the reuse of cell resources. It can increase the frequency spectrum efficiency of the cellular communication system and reduce the terminal transmitting power, solving the problem of frequency spectrum resource shortage of the wireless communication system to some extent.

The traditional cellular communication system takes the base station as the center to realize the cell coverage because the base station cannot move with the coverage area and the network structure has limited flexibility. With the increase of wireless multimedia services, the service requirements in various complex environments challenge the traditional base-centered network approach.

D2D technology can realize direct communication between communication terminals without the help of a base station and expand network connection and access methods, as shown in Fig. 2.9. Due to short distance direct communication and high channel quality, D2D can achieve higher data rate, lower delay, and lower power consumption. Through the widely distributed terminal, the coverage can be improved to realize the efficient utilization of spectrum resources. Also, it can support more flexible network architecture and connection methods to improve link flexibility and Internet reliability.

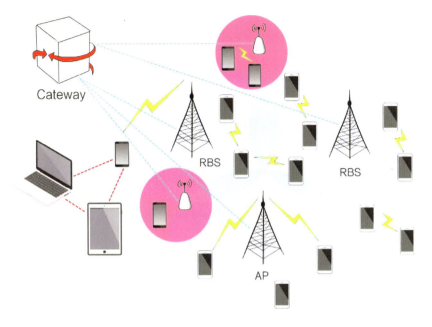

Figure 2.9 End-to-end communication technology.

V2V (Vehicle-to-Vehicle) communication in Internet of Vehicles is a typical D2D communication application scenario enhanced by Internet of Things. Each vehicle-mounted unit can communicate directly with vehicle-mounted units in other nearby vehicles without the need to forward by base stations or RSUS. In this way, the communication delay between vehicles can be greatly reduced and the transmission rate can be greatly improved. During high-speed driving, vehicle operation actions such as the lane changes and deceleration can be intimated with an early warning through D2D communication. When other surrounding vehicles receive the warning, they can warn the driver according to it or even conduct autonomous control of the vehicle in an emergency so as to shorten the response time of the driver in an emergency and reduce the traffic accident rate. In addition, D2D technology enables vehicles to more reliably detect and identify specific vehicles in their vicinity, such as potentially dangerous vehicles passing through intersections and vehicles with special use requiring special attention (such as vehicles carrying dangerous goods and school buses). D2D based on terminal pass-through has unique advantages in the field of vehicle networking security due to its characteristics in communication delay and proximity discovery.

2.2.2.6 High-precision positioning

Vehicle high-precision positioning technology is an indispensable key technology to realize intelligent transportation and automatic driving. The business applications of Internet of Vehicles mainly include traffic safety, traffic efficiency, information service, and automatic driving. Typical traffic safety services include intersection collision warning, emergency braking warning, etc. Typical traffic efficiency services include speed guidance, emergency vehicle avoidance, etc. Typical information services include near-field payment, map download, and so on. Positioning accuracy is the most basic requirement of a positioning service. In different business applications and scenarios, positioning accuracy requirements are different. For example, auxiliary driving requires positioning accuracy at the meter level, while autonomous driving requires positioning accuracy at the sub-meter level or even at the centimeter level.

In different scenarios and environments, the performance index requirements of each business application positioning can be satisfied to ensure the stability and reliability of positioning, which is the prerequisite to carry out the Internet of Vehicles business. Cars, as moving entities, will pass through different scenes, such as tunnels, highways, dense urban areas, as well as underground garages and will be affected by different environments, such as light, weather, and shielding. Considering the complex environment, scene, as well as factors such as cost and stability, only a certain location technology cannot satisfy the requirement of the networking business car positioning. We often have to use a variety of technology integration to achieve accurate positioning, including GNSS (Global Navigation Satellite System), radio (such as cellular networks and local area network), map of inertial measurement unit, sensors, and maps with high precision.

Among the kinematic algorithms, GNSS based on Real-time Kinematic Differential Technology (RTK) is the most basic positioning method. GNSS technology can reach centimeter level in an outdoor open environment without shielding, but its performance is poor in shielding scenes, tunnels, dense urban areas, and other scenes. So, its application scene is limited to the outdoor environment. Sensor-based positioning is another common method for vehicle positioning, but high cost, poor sensitivity to the environment, and slow mapping and updating speed limit the rapid popularization of sensor positioning. Single technologies such as GNSS or sensors cannot guarantee the high-precision positioning performance of vehicles in any environment. Therefore, some other auxiliary methods, such as inertial navigation, high-precision map, and cellular network, will be combined to improve positioning accuracy and stability. Among them, the cellular network is crucial in improving positioning performance. For example, the 5G cellular network can support real-time transmission of RTK data and sensor data and real-time updating of high-precision maps. In addition, the positioning capability of 5G itself also provides strong support for high-precision positioning of vehicles.

In the context of the rapid development and popularization of 5G and C-V2X, combined with the scene analysis and performance requirements for vehicle high-precision positioning, the network architecture of vehicle high-precision positioning system mainly includes terminal layer, network layer, platform layer, and application layer, as shown in Fig. 2.10. Among them, the terminal layer realizes multi-source data fusion (satellite, sensor, and cellular network data) algorithm to ensure the positioning

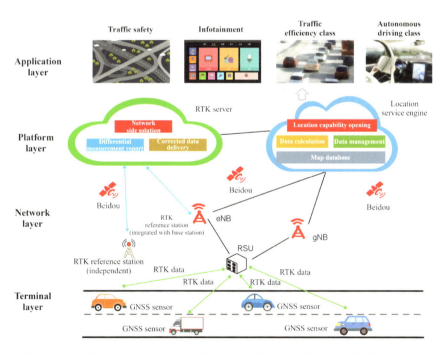

Figure 2.10 Network architecture of the vehicle high-precision positioning system.

46   *The World of 5G: Intelligent Transportation*

requirements of different application scenarios and different services. The network layer includes 5G base station, RTK base station, and roadside unit to help the positioning terminal realize reliable data transmission. The platform layer provides integrated vehicle positioning functions, including differential calculation ability, map database, HD dynamic map, positioning engine, and open positioning capability. The application layer based on the high-precision positioning system can provide lane-level navigation, route planning, automatic driving, and other functions for the application layer.

2.2.2.7 *C-V2X*

V2X, as the name suggests, is a car to connect everything. It is the soul of the Internet of Vehicles. According to the connected objects, they can be divided into VaV (Vehicles and Vehicles), V2I (Vehicles and Infrastructure), V2P (Vehicles and Pedestrians), and V2N (Vehicles and Internet), as shown in Fig. 2.11.

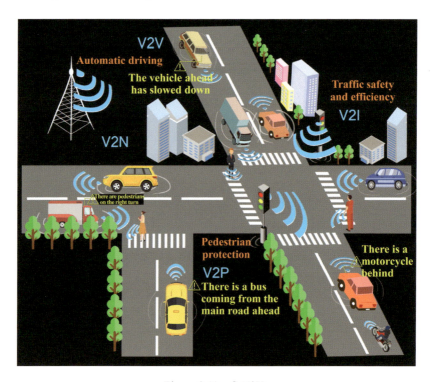

Figure 2.11   C-V2X.

V2X can be used for all kinds of anti-collision, anti-rolled-over reminder, collision warning, overtaking collision warning, traffic jam queue warning, blind spot warning at intersections, curve deceleration warning, etc. In addition to collision prevention, it can also realize cruise control, driving formation control, intelligent fleet control, and other vehicle coordination functions to make the vehicle running on the road more orderly and efficient.

C-V2X is V2X based on cellular mobile communication technology. Early V2X was based primarily on DSRC. C-V2X, as a rising star, supports two communication interfaces which are cellular communication interface (Uu) and direct-connect communication interface (PC5). Cellular networks have a feature of wider coverage, while direct-connect communication interfaces allow cars to communicate directly with other vehicles, roadside units, and other infrastructures to give a faster response.

Compared with DSRC, C-V2X has the following advantages:

(1) Less interference between users, more concurrent users, and a reliable connection can be maintained in high-density vehicle deployment scenarios.
(2) Based on the cellular communication network, the effective communication distance becomes long, providing the driver with a longer braking response time.
(3) With 4G and 5G cellular mobile communication network reuse, the deployment cost will be reduced.
(4) With a wider network coverage, it can provide early warnings for remote events.
(5) 3GPP has formulated a unified global standard, convenient for the use of a single chipset with the module cost greatly reduced too.
(6) C-V2X, as an important part of 5G, continues to evolve and the technology continues to upgrade.

Due to the leading technology, C-V2X has been widely supported by many industries such as transportation, automobile, and communication, becoming the most advanced technical standard to realize the development of the intelligent network. The industry chain of C-V2X technology is gradually maturing with the loading rate of C-V2X on-board terminals constantly upgrading and the roadside infrastructure constantly improving. It is believed that in the near future, the Internet of Vehicles based on the C-V2X standard will be within reach.

2.2.3 The best fit between intelligent transportation and 5G

Like a catalyst, 5G will expedite the deep integration of high and new technologies such as the Internet of Things, Big Data, cloud computing, and artificial intelligence, bringing the development of intelligent transportation into the fast track while making unprecedented reforms in the entire transportation industry.

2.2.3.1 5G and the Internet of Vehicles

The Internet of Vehicles is one of the hot technologies in recent years. Thanks to the features of 5G, such as ultra-low delay, ultra-high transmission bandwidth, and ultra-large connection, the two main lines of Internet of Vehicles, which are "safety" and "intelligence", have developed rapidly. The 5G ultra-large connection is the basis for the realization of C-V2X technology for vehicle networking as well as the basis for the interconnection between cars and everything. 5G's ultra-low latency and ultra-high transmission bandwidth ensure the realization of the most anticipated application of vehicle networking technology, autonomous driving technology. The massive data collected by cameras and sensors are needed for rapid interaction with cloud traffic facilities and other traffic participants in the process of vehicle driving. The communication of such data needs to be supported by a channel with sufficient bandwidth and extremely low latency, which is fundamental for the 5G network to assist automatic driving. 5G empowers driverless cars, which is reflected not only in the highly reliable data interaction and collaborative computing but also in more precise perception. 5G can improve the perception accuracy and make the perception fusion better on car's, road's, and cloud's end as the accelerator for implementing autonomous driving.

2.2.3.2 5G and intelligent vehicle–road collaborative system

A smart car-and-road coordination system is based on wireless communication, sensing detection technology for vehicle-and-road information. Intelligent coordination and cooperation between vehicles and infrastructures are realized through information interaction and sharing between vehicles and vehicles as well as vehicles and roads to ensure traffic safety, improve traffic efficiency, and reduce urban pollution. Therefore, a safe, efficient, and environmentally friendly road traffic system is formed.

The intelligent vehicle–road collaborative system has three main features. First, it pays attention to the overall coordination of man–road–vehicle. Second, it lays emphasis on large-scale network control. Third, it tries to make full use of various modes of traffic network and information interaction. These characteristics highlight the importance of the support from wireless communication networks in intelligent vehicle–road collaboration. With the arrival of 5G, the intelligent vehicle–road collaboration system will be gradually improved. The integration of road network, sensing network, control network, energy network, and management database platform will be accelerated to realize the simultaneous operation of intelligent vehicles of different levels on the same road so as to achieve vehicle–road collaboration.

2.2.3.3 *5G digital and intelligent road signs*

With the development of 5G, China's highways will accelerate digitalization and intelligent transformation. Road signs and rules will undergo intelligent transformation. In the future, road signs (such as "road construction ahead, please slow down") and traffic lights will be able to autonomously coordinate and control the passage time of vehicles and pedestrians according to road conditions. In the future, virtual traffic light technology will also appear, which will hand the right of driving and right of way to every car driving near the intersection and let them "collectively vote" to decide whether a certain car in a certain direction should pass or stop. It will remind the driver in the form of traffic light through the on-board display or head-up display technology. This means that every car is equipped with a traffic light system telling the car to go on or stop.

2.2.3.4 *5G and highway barrier-free toll*

There are many reasons for highway congestion, among which the highway toll is one of the most important reasons. With the development of 5G, barrier-free tolls will be fully covered on expressways. On the exclusive ETC lanes, the relevant platform system will accurately locate the driving cars in real time. When cars enter the automatic billing section, the automatic settlement system will calculate the highway toll of the driving cars and generate toll information. After the driving cars receive the electronic toll information, the owner can later make independent online payment through the website, eliminating the process of stopping the car to pay the toll. Once the expressway barrier-free toll work gets on the right track, the expressway will be equipped with no bar instead of automatic bar lifting, realizing fast traffic without stopping.

2.2.3.5 *5G pre-identification of road accidents*

In the intelligent traffic management system, road accident identification is an important basis for intelligent transportation management. At present, road accident identification mainly relies on cameras and other equipment to collect the image of road traffic monitoring area and then to identify the vehicles on the road and vehicle collision events. Along with the development of the 5G, in the future, smart cameras will perform a structural analysis on the images of vehicles on the road. They can predict the status of the vehicles during a short period of time before the accident occurs to prevent vehicle collision events from happening. It means that through a variety of means (such as artificial intelligent video-analyzing technology), smart cameras will provide early warnings of accidents on highways so as to achieve multi-state identification of road traffic accidents ahead of time and avoid traffic accidents. This pre-identification capability is also the focus of the future development of the security industry.

2.3 The Significance of the Implementation of Transportation

2.3.1 *The plan for intelligent transportation*

Intelligent transportation is not only an important part of the construction of smart cities but also one of the important means to exalt the governance capacity of the governments and realize the modernization of national governance. The experience of Japan, the United States, and other countries with good development of intelligent transportation shows that the early unified top-level planning contributed a lot. The successful implementation of smart bus and BRT (Bus Rapid Transit) and other intelligent transportation applications in various pilot cities in China also benefited from the unified planning of the competent government departments in the early stage and the unified coordination in the later implementation.

Intelligent transportation is a huge and complex system. Participants in intelligent transportation involve government, enterprises, institutions, public, etc. The data and resource sharing involves cross-department, cross-field, etc., which require the government to take the lead in breaking down information and resources barriers such as departments, institutions, and fields, fully integrating information resources, and doing a good job in top-level design. At the same time, intelligent transportation, a system that can be achieved overnight, requires enterprises and scientific research institutions to continue with unremitting follow-up research under the orientation of market demand toward in-depth and intelligent development through continuous technological advancement.

The top-level design of intelligent transportation should put requirement analysis in the first place, which can mainly start from the two dimensions of user requirement and functional requirement. The participants of user requirement generally include the government and the public. The government hopes to integrate the data resources of the transportation industry and make macro decisions such as urban development planning, traffic requirement management, and coordinated emergency response. Traffic management departments hope to put forward their own requirements in traffic monitoring, traffic command and guidance, traffic law enforcement, vehicle and driver management, traffic safety, traffic management facilities, etc. The public prefers to plan before travel, guide during travel, and provide diversified personalized services. The functional requirements should be based on local actual requirements and oriented by actual business requirements. Functional requirements generally include traffic monitoring, decision support, traffic control and command, traffic law enforcement, integrated application of traffic management, integrated traffic information services, etc.

Intelligent transportation should be comprehensively planned on the principles with people at the center to serve people's livelihood under the guidance of requirements through intelligent, efficient, green, and low-carbon development driven by innovations to save energy and protect the environment. Relying on advanced technologies and fully considering the personalized needs of travelers, it should provide travelers with an intimate, safe, and efficient travel experience. Ultimately, transportation efficiency will be greatly improved. Traffic control will be accurate and intelligent. Traffic information will be comprehensive and timely. Furthermore, traffic experiences will be comfortable and fast with a low-carbon and energy-saving transportation system.

2.3.2 *The framework for intelligent transportation*

The overall framework of intelligent transportation can be generally divided into four levels, i.e., data acquisition, data resource sharing and analysis, data business application, and command and decision visualization.

The following is the overall framework of intelligent transportation in a city, which is divided into four parts, i.e., traffic Big Data collection and data center, traffic Big Data sharing and analysis platform, traffic Big Data business application platform, and traffic Big Data command and decision visualization platform, as shown in Fig. 2.12.

2.3.2.1 *Traffic Big Data acquisition and data center*

The Traffic Big Data Acquisition and Data Center has established a unified data standard and directory system of traffic Big Data, mainly including (but is not limited to) basic information database of traffic industry, GIS (Geographic Information System) database, video database, etc. All kinds of traffic data are collected, reviewed, classified, queried, and counted to form the basic database of the traffic industry, which meets the demand expansion of the database. After its expansion, the overall system operation will not be affected.

2.3.2.2 *Traffic Big Data sharing and analysis platform*

The Traffic Big Data Sharing and Analysis platform is the core of the traffic brain. It adopts Big Data, AI, image recognition, cloud computing, and other technologies to realize the collection, integration, cleaning, mining, computing analysis, business modeling, model display, and other functions of traffic Big Data, outputting the analysis results in various display ways.

2.3.2.3 *Traffic Big Data business application platform*

By integrating the data of multiple service systems, a special Big Data analysis platform is established to realize data analysis and decision-making for railway transport, road passenger transport, urban taxi, freight transport, water transport, bus network, and other services in the whole field of transportation.

Power of Intelligent Transportation Redoubled with the Support of 5G 53

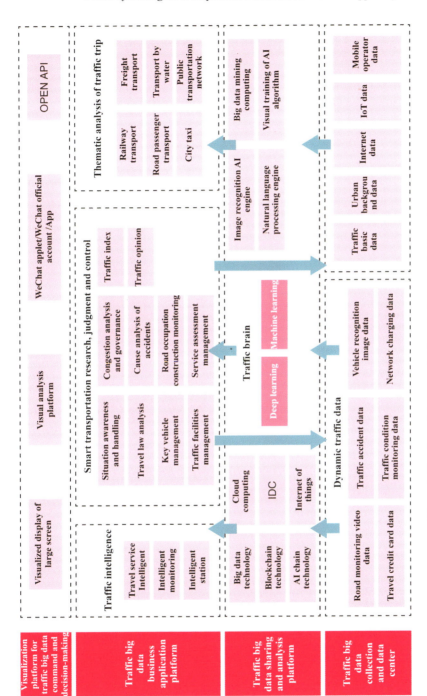

Figure 2.12 Overall framework of smart transportation in a city.

2.3.2.4 Traffic Big Data command and decision visualization platform

Big Data is visualized on a large HD screen to achieve a comprehensive data display. The platform provides personalized presentation based on the content and type of data access, data characteristics, etc., in an intuitive, simple, and visual manner.

> The convenient travel mode and efficient traffic management mode are expected in the future. The future traffic management mode and transportation mode reform are subversive with 5G as the basis for the realization of this change. By deeply merging new technologies such as Big Data, Internet, artificial intelligence, block chain, and cloud computing into the transportation industry to promote the development of transportation enabled by data resources, 5G will finally help to build an efficient, convenient, safe, green, and economic intelligent transportation system. The key technologies of 5G (edge computing, ultra-dense networking, large-scale MIMO, network slicing, end-to-end communication, high-precision positioning, and 5G-based C-V2X) will enable 5G to perform well in the three application scenarios with enhanced broadband, high reliability, low latency, and large-scale machine communication in the transportation industry. The peak user rate of 5G reaches the standard of 10–100 Gb/s, meeting the requirements of high-definition video and other Big Data transmission. The delay level of air interface reaches millisecond level, meeting the requirements of real-time application such as automatic pilot. A super large network capacity provides the connection capacity of millions of devices per square kilometer to meet the needs of Internet of Vehicles communication. Under continuous wide area coverage and high mobility, the user experience rate reaches 0.1–1 Gb/s, supporting mobility of 500 km/h.
>
> The future intelligent transportation architecture integrates the new configuration of the interconnection of everything to be an interactive mode of high-order full perception, which can meet the functional requirements of different periods, azimuth monitoring, and other application scenarios to the greatest extent. 5G wireless transmission network, the key technology to construct the intelligent transportation system, can avoid more geographical restrictions. The construction of the intelligent transportation system requires the top-level design of relevant national departments,

cross-departmental and cross-field coordination, and the participation from all sectors of society. Only by adhering to the principles of putting people first, serving people's livelihood, putting requirements as a guide, overall planning, innovation-driven development, green and low-carbon development, energy conservation and environmental protection, and intelligent and efficient construction, can we build a modern intelligent transportation system with high quality.

Chapter 3
Better Life and Smart Travel with 5G+

The development of communication technologies impelled communication tools such as mobile phones to gradually evolve into intelligent terminals. Meanwhile, the application of the new generation of technology in Vehicle to Everything (V2X) has also realized remote vehicle control, Big Data early warning, real-time navigation and enabled us to communicate with the world anytime and anywhere, which makes our travel more convenient and fun.

In terms of the current industry trends, in the future, 5G may bring significant changes to transportation in the following aspects:

First of all, 5G will greatly promote the technological upgrade in V2X and driverless vehicles, contributing to the formation of new types of shared cars.

Second, thanks to intelligent driving, each car is connected in order to determine each other's position.

The rise of the 5G network enables communication carriers to provide automotive safety applications with exceptionally fast response speed by part of the network slice. Even driving with a speed of up to 120 km/h, the time for cars to respond is still sufficient, as the response speed of smart cars will be milliseconds. Given such speed, cars can be safer, especially for the most common application scenario in autonomous driving. For example, emergency braking requires instantaneous processing of large amounts of data and timely decision-making. All of these rely on the collaborative completion of 5G's outstanding capabilities, such as large broadband, the ultra-high number of connections, high reliability, and accuracy.

Finally, service informatization, such as high-precision maps, will dominate 5G intelligent transportation as navigation products we use now such as Baidu Maps and Amap still have a certain degree of deviation in practical application. Compared to the existing maps, the high-precision maps can locate almost all objects on the road through their information as they are based on 5G. Moreover, with these maps, the real-time changes in the monitoring vehicle and the surrounding objects identified by it can be uploaded through the 5G network to achieve accurate positioning.

3.1 More Convenient Travel with Informationized Service

3.1.1 *Information query and planning of travels*

In recent years, urban residents have been faced with serious traffic problems due to accelerated urbanization and economic development. One of these problems is traffic congestion, which has caused serious inconvenience to the daily life of residents. Solving this difficult problem of travel has become an urgent demand of the public, so the travel information service arises at this historic moment.

The travel information service aims to guide residents to travel intelligently, which involves the application of high-end technologies such as mobile Internet and electronic technology in the field of transportation, providing traffic information for residents. In this way, the transportation service can be improved for them to enjoy a higher level of comfort and convenience.

This service includes many aspects, among which travel information inquiry and planning witness the widest application and greatest requirement.

3.1.1.1 *Travel information inquiry*

Most of us are faced with travel problems every day, such as commuting to work, traveling by car, or returning home during holidays. The first step we should do before going out is to inquire about travel information. How can we get there, by car or by public transport? Train or plane? Car or ship? Are there any traffic jams on the road? Do the roads have traffic control? Have the train tickets been sold out? Is there any discount on air tickets? How many people are there? What's the weather like? and so on, as shown in Fig. 3.1. If the destination is a tourist attraction, can I buy a ticket in advance? How is the queue at the scenic spot? These are the questions that we often care about every time we travel. Our query contains information about public transportation including static and dynamic service information (hub congestion, line of travel, as well as bus and subway schedules/running state), traffic information (traffic congestion), routing information (traffic accident information ahead), and related supporting facilities information (location of gas stations and public toilets). In addition, we also need to inquire about weather information (rain, shine, snow, and other weather conditions) in the process of travel.

Due to the development and popularity of mobile Internet and the abundance of travel service application products, we can obtain a lot of information we need to query in a timely manner, which to a large extent meets our needs for travel information. However, we will still encounter many problems in use. Besides the color block display, is there any video on the congested route? What is the condition of the station now? Where does the bus or subway go? Can I view the video image information of the tourist destination? These problems are limited by the level of technology development and the richness of product applications.

The integration and development of Big Data, cloud computing, Internet of Things, and other technologies based on the 5G network make it possible to meet the above needs. The 5G network has the characteristics of enhanced mobile broadband, large-scale machine communication, high reliability, and low delay, so that everything can be connected and information can be exchanged in time. The characteristic of high bandwidth can greatly improve the quality and efficiency of road surveillance video transmission; 5G's edge computing capacity can be deployed nearby through AI algorithms, which improves the ability of traffic data processing and prediction. The application of Big Data, cloud computing, and AI technology can conduct rapid retrieval and statistical analysis of massive data as well as in-depth association analysis to dig out valuable information and improve the efficiency of large-scale traffic linkage scheduling.

Imagine the future, if there is traffic congestion, the driving system has already done a prediction analysis on the following traffic conditions

60　*The World of 5G: Intelligent Transportation*

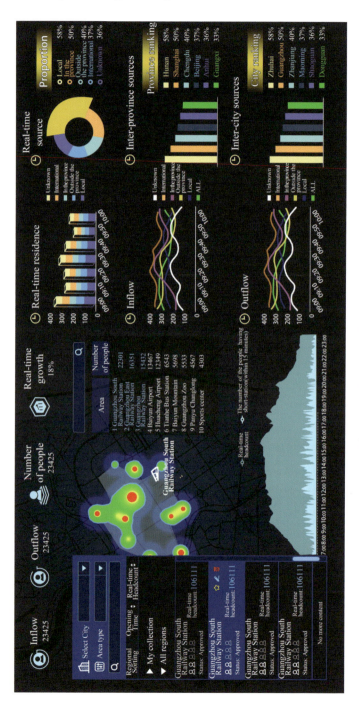

Figure 3.1　Passenger flow statistics.

through Big Data and has made accurate prediction and congestion avoidance schemes for you. You can also watch a video of the traffic along the route to see what's happening. You can check the queuing situation through the station network live broadcast. Wearable devices can tell you where your bus or subway is at anytime, instead of making you anxiously wait for your bus or subway. A live video of the scenic spot can be used to check out the parking lot of the scenic spot. The Internet of Everything based on the 5G network breaks down the barrier between any device, traffic facilities, and traffic management department data. You can find out information not only through a few maps travel software but also through any wearable devices, smart home terminals, vehicle-mounted smart terminals, and other devices at anytime and anywhere.

3.1.1.2 *Travel planning*

After the relevant travel information was searched, the next thing we need to do is travel planning. Just think about it, which issue do we care about most every time we travel? It's how we can get to our destination in least time and distance or reasonably pass through those places where we need to go according to our preconceived ideas and then get to our destination. In the face of complex and changeable traffic conditions, the accurate estimation of travel time is affected by many factors, such as whether it is the rush hour, how is the road condition, whether there is a traffic accident or temporary control, whether the weather conditions are conducive to traffic, and so on. Good travel planning can accurately estimate the travel time for travelers, according to the departure place, destination, travel set, the most appropriate route, and accurate estimation of time. Therefore, travel planning is aimed at the travel route of travelers from the starting point to the end point. Good travel planning is to choose the optimal route among multiple travel routes.

Travel planning in the 5G era is no longer the simple travel planning that we commonly use in the map software, but the real-time transmission of personal travel demand, travel preference, and driving habits to the cloud. It will be perfectly matched with traffic facilities, traffic stations, travel tools, and parking services to form information sharing. According to the travel needs of each person, a reasonable travel planning will be matched out.

3.1.2 Vehicle navigation and guidance of vehicle movement

> For example, when you're sent on a business trip from your company, it only takes one hour to get to the airport from home. But due to the temporary closure of the road under construction near the airport, you need to change the route, which will take nearly half an hour longer than the normal travel time. In this case, Big Data prediction can be "foretold" by calculating and recommending the most suitable and comfortable travel route for travelers with its estimated time on the basis of analysis and prediction on all the traffic-related data and information collected, careful consideration on the road restrictions, construction, traffic lights, and other information at the time of departure as well as comprehensive synthesis of the road conditions, route time at the same moment in history, and the personal habits of the travelers.
>
> Let's imagine again. Early in the morning one day, you are awakened by an intelligent sound box, and the smart speaker tells you "The weather is clear today, and it is appropriate for an outing". Then, you brush your teeth in front of a mirror listing several destinations suitable for an outing for you to choose. When you choose the destination, the mirror will send the destination information to navigation automatically. After that, the car's navigation makes an accurate estimate and tells you through a smart speaker which road will be the most convenient at which time. Is it cool to think about it? In fact, it is also a part of travel information inquiry and planning, and everything will become reality with the application of 5G.

As mentioned above, travel planning can offer an optimal route according to the pre-built prediction model when travelers are blocked by congestion. How can one formulate the optimal route? The answer is closely related to the following topic: vehicle navigation and driving guidance.

3.1.2.1 Vehicle navigation

In the 4G era, most of the mapping software we use are convenient and clear. Despite that, there are still some errors.

Many people are familiar with Chongqing, which is also known as "the 3D magic city". Chongqing became popular in 2017 because of the complex 5-layer-and-20-ramp Huang Jue Bay overpass, which will take you around Chongqing if you choose the wrong ramp. As such, this overpass makes all the navigation systems shift their blame.

Of course, the above-mentioned story is but a showcase that the map navigation software in use in the 4G era failed to give accurate positioning in some sections of complicated terrain though it can be enough in most cases under the network of 4G era, and this is strong evidence that we should call for the 5G network with its greater strengths. With 5G, every mapping software will be equipped with high-precision positioning, so that high-precision positioning, ultra-fine rendering and voice-free wake-up service can be put in place in the map service. Compared to the existing Global Positioning System (GPS), the navigation errors, supported by 5G, will decrease greatly. For instance, the signal attenuation in tunnels or viaducts in the past, the gray navigation interface, as well as the anchor point drift will be greatly reduced. 5G will be able to locate almost every object on the road, and its base stations with high density can effectively improve the stability of the network signal as well as the amount of information about the position. Simultaneously, indoor positioning with high accuracy of sub-meter level can be realized in the signal blind area based on the amount of information. Besides that, through the 5G network, the real-time changes in the monitored vehicles and the surrounding objects identified can be uploaded to the map inside the car. Therefore, positioning accuracy can be improved.

3.1.2.2 *Driving guidance*

As noted previously, travel planning can help us to avoid traffic jams in a timely manner. However, sometimes, road congestion is inevitable under the current road conditions. For instance, during the Spring Festival, the highway traffic increases rapidly so we have to take some congested roads when traveling back home. In this case, it is necessary to have good driving guidance methods to ease the traffic congestion in time.

Then, what is driving induction? To put it simply, driving guidance aims to improve traffic by guiding the travel behavior of road users, so that the time for vehicles to stay on the road can be reduced. Eventually, the traffic flow can be distributed reasonably in each section of the road network so as to prevent traffic jams. Driving guidance can provide road users with optimal path guidance instruction based on the traveler's departure and destination. With the guidance, road users are able to find an optimal path according to the real-time traffic information, which depends on the support from modern technologies such as electronics, computers, the Internet, and communication.

When it comes to the transportation/traveling during the periods around Spring Festival, I believe, more or less, that people have experienced difficulties such as struggling to grab a ticket, being congested along the highway, or running into the crowd of passenger flow at major airports and railway stations, which has left a very poor impression among most of us, but this can be solved through the functions of driving guidance.

On January 11, 2020, according to the characteristics of the rush, the first "Spring Festival transportation forecasting system" was launched in a map software under the guidance of Department of Transport Services, Ministry of Transport. The system included "The Rush Forecast", "The Rush Real-time Broadcast", as well as "The Migration across Cities during the Rush", as shown in Fig. 3.2.

"The Rush Forecast" can predict the expressway congestion in most provinces and cities (24 provinces and 50 cities) in the next seven days. "The Rush Real-time Broadcast" can present the real-time congestion situation in the national expressway network, railway stations, airports, and tollbooths. In addition, the data will be updated every two minutes. You can check the popular migration routes in key regions such as Beijing-Tianjin-Hebei, the

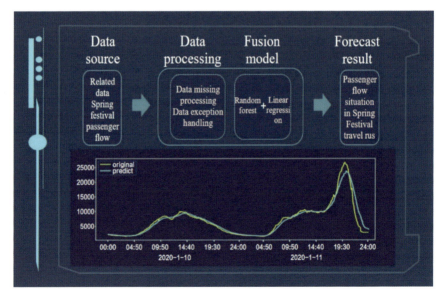

Figure 3.2 The Rush Forecast.

Yangtze River Delta, the Pearl River Delta, Chengdu, and Chongqing the day before. The system can obtain massive traffic data in various channels such as video equipment, products of Internet of Things, and the Internet. Moreover, highway conditions and information about the event can be identified with the help of artificial intelligence data fusion and 5G technology. In addition to the rush, the system can provide decision-making references for the competent departments of the transportation industry. At the same time, the management party can be reminded timely for planning, and users can be informed in a timely manner. Eventually, passengers are able to make reasonable travel arrangements, so that their travel will be safe and smooth at a high speed.

During the rush, a large number of motorcyclists return home from other places. Accordingly, the first motorcycle navigation in China was launched in the software. The navigation can help users effectively avoid traffic control while informing the users about the weather forecasts and safety tips along the way according to the rules of traffic control of the city and different motorcycle license plates. Equipped with the software, the crowd can form a team taking the same route to return home. The team feature also allows the sharing of locations by the motorcyclists, which can prevent them from getting lost.

The above-mentioned process can be put in place because of the increasingly mature development of communication technology. The 5G technology and real-time status reported by a large number of users and the cooperation between the software and traffic management departments allow us to obtain real-time authoritative data. Generally speaking, it makes return more comfortable, provides great convenience, and makes science and technology more user-friendly. Moreover, we have to realize that the future development of transportation cannot be achieved without modern information technology and the participation from the government as well as the entire country.

3.1.3 *Electronic toll collection (ETC) and non-inductive payment*

3.1.3.1 *ETC*

Since 2019, the abolition of provincial tollbooths has become a hot topic issue of social concern. How can one abolish them to achieve barrier-free charge? The answer is to promote ETC, as shown in Fig. 3.3.

66 *The World of 5G: Intelligent Transportation*

Figure 3.3 ETC toll station.

What is ETC? It is the electronic non-parking toll collection system, which is also known as the automatic road toll collection system. The system is commonly used for automatic toll collection in highways or bridges through electronic tags installed on the windshield of vehicles. These on-board tags will conduct short-range communication with the RSU ETC lane in the toll station. Next, real-time settlement in the back end is conducted through the computer networking technology and the bank. Therefore, the toll can be paid when people are driving through the tollbooths on highways or bridges without parking.

On May 10, 2019, Dai Dongchang, Vice Minister of the Ministry of Transport, said that the usage of ETC should reach more than 90% by the end of 2019 to ensure the smooth operation of the entire road network after the abolition of provincial tollbooths. China has issued a series of policies to ensure the smooth operation of the entire road network. The main reason behind this lies in the fact that ETC is particularly suitable to be used in expressways or highways, bridges, and tunnels with heavy traffic.

At present, special ETC lanes are built-in toll gates of all expressways in China, which only requires car owners to install the On-Board Unit (OBU) in their cars. Known as transponders or electronic tags, these units are also installed on the windshield of the vehicle. When the vehicle passes through a toll gate, the car can be detected by the RSU installed in the ETC lane, and the RSU will send an interrogation signal, which will be responded to by the OBU. The above communication of information between the RSU and the OBU is achieved through the microwave. Following that, the car can be identified automatically based on a series of background data processing in the central management system. If the car can be identified, the billing and deduction will be carried out. Then, a signal will be sent to the banister controller to release the car. If the car fails to pass the identification, an alarm will be sent by the alarmer until the vehicle goes beyond the range of the sensor. As shown in Fig. 3.4, during this whole process, the communication between the OBU and RSU is very quick while the computing speed of the system is very fast. In fact, it takes less than two seconds to collect the toll for each car. The car owner does not need to pay the toll manually by stopping the car. Compared to the manual toll payment process, the automatic toll collection can not only improve the traffic efficiency greatly but also allow the management of toll collection of roads to become paperless and cashless. As a result, low efficiency of fee charges can be avoided while keeping it environmentally friendly.

According to the data released by the Ministry of Transport, the number of new ETC users surpassed 120 million in 2019. The accumulated

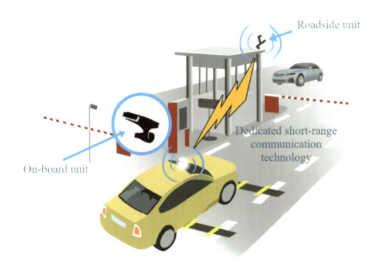

Figure 3.4 Principle of ETC.

total number of ETC users nationwide reached 204 million by the end of 2019, and at the same time, ETC coverage has risen significantly. Moreover, the use of ETC has been gradually extended from high-speed traffic of single way to car consumption scenes such as parking, refueling, and car washing. ETC, as a tool for vehicle mobile payment, is gradually becoming an access point to intelligent transportation services. It is believed that in the near future, the comprehensive perception of infrastructure, road transportation, and traffic flow can be established based on the ETC. Then, the content of the perception can be transmitted to vehicle users and city managers, which is the beginning of the intelligent integration of traffic and cars. To put it simply, cars can be "smarter" through the ETC which connects roads as well as cars, respectively, so as to serve people with the content of connection.

However, with the rollout of ETC, problems come one after another, such as unreasonable deductions, fraudulent charges, system instability, busy customer service line, and offline business hall queuing. Admittedly, ETC is facing great challenges; however, from the perspective of long-term development, smart transportation can be further developed supported by the maturity of technologies such as 5G, driverless cars, and V2X. In the future, intelligent electronic tags especially those with 5G mobile communication ability will be further developed. They will be able to meet the requirement of ETC free flow toll while enriching the content of the information interaction between the road and the car. Therefore, a complete basic frame of intelligent electronic tags, intelligent roadside equipment (IRE), and cloud infrastructure can be formed in advance for the transition to vehicle–road collaboration technology. The ETC technology will be integrated more actively with new technologies, such as mobile payment, electronic license plate, and high-definition video recognition with mapping information technology and BeiDou high-precision positioning. After the integration, ETC can achieve higher recognition accuracy and faster transaction speed, offering a clearer picture for online development.

3.1.3.2 *Non-inductive payment*

In the path of realizing the "non-inductive payment" for cars, there has been a debate about two solutions, which are terminal ETC equipment and machine vision-based license plate recognition. These two solutions have been successfully implemented in commercial cases according to various national conditions of different countries. Objectively speaking, the scene applications of both ETC and license plate recognition have their own pros and cons, respectively.

The advantage of ETC lies in its strengthening the regulation that a vehicle can only be bound by one plate. Despite that, electromagnetic wave transmission is vulnerable to interference, and equipment failure is very common. The license plate recognition is more user-friendly, without the reliance on on-board terminals. However, it has certain disadvantages including ineffective avoidance of illegal behaviors, such as using a set of sign vehicles based on 2D visual technical principles having drawbacks.

People are looking forward to a safe and convenient solution for non-inductive payment for cars so that it will be unnecessary to install a wide range of terminals such as the ETC. It is very promising that such a solution can emerge with the development of 3D vision technology.

At present, the 3D vision technology is widely applied in the field of mobile payment. Its technical principle is based on a 3D vision sensor to capture the three-dimensional information of objects. Moreover, its detection precision can reach the security level of financial payment. Through the 3D vision technology, the 3D image of a car is collected in order to carry out the extraction and analysis of multiple features. In this way, it is easy to identify whether the model is in line with the license plate information. The extensive application of the technology may eliminate the problem of using a set of sign plates to a large extent to achieve high efficiency and safety.

Whether it is 3D vision technology or ETC, in terms of their operation logic, it can be easily found that the development trend of the non-inductive payment aims to get rid of the bondage and tie of media for the users. In that case, money can be paid "in a senseless way" with higher security management. The 3D vision technology plays a key role in the application scenes of people and cars. With the technology, machine intelligent terminals are able to "understand" everything to become an important link in the development of smart transportation in the future. The fundamental demands of its development are to attain efficient operation and safe upgrading, whether it is implemented in the non-inductive payment or the improvement of traffic security.

Our wild imagination has been gradually turned into reality, from the early stages of laboratory tests to building efficient and safe intelligent transportation in the future. In the future path of intelligent transportation development, 5G and AI will be the cornerstones to drive the intelligent

Internet of Everything. The 3D visual non-inductive payment will play its full role in the field of transportation to achieve great success.

3.2 Safer Travels with Smart Driving

5G is characterized by its super-high bandwidth, super-low time delay, and super-large access. Through 5G, the communication channel between cars and the outside world can be widened, so that cars can be connected to everything and transportation will be safer. Thanks to the low-latency communication of 5G, the collaboration between vehicles and roads can be possible. Supported by cloud computing, the development of intelligent driving systems can reach a higher speed. Connecting all the smart devices, 5G makes the city integrated as a whole, which is the only way leading to smart transportation.

3.2.1 *The classification of smart driving*

The International Society of Automotive Engineers (SAE) divides driving into six levels, which are L0–L5, in terms of the classification of the smart drive:

> **L0:** Human driving, with only warnings and without driving assistance system.
> **L1:** Human driving assisted with systems, such as the adaptive cruise and steering control system, to achieve the automation of steering control or single speed, but still driven by a man.
> **L2:** Partially automated driving, which can realize the automation of speed and steering control, but the driver must always be monitoring, such as keeping the car in the center of the road.
> **L3:** Autopilot under certain conditions, achieving hands-off for drivers but drivers must be focused in case of emergency.
> **L4:** Advanced autopilot is achieved so drivers can take their eyes off, and no driver intervention is required in some predefined scenes.
> **L5:** Full autopilot is achieved, and no driver is needed.

L0 refers to manual driving. L1–L2 can be defined as the automatic driving assistance system. L3–L5 can be regarded as the autopilot system. In L5, the autopilot system can reach the level of a human driver and it is able to deal with all road conditions.

3.2.2 Smart driving at present

At present, the smart drive is in the L2 and L3 stages. The smart drive is based on a single car, which means cars are installed with sensors, such as multiple cameras, millimeter-wave radars, and laser radars. These sensors act as the "eyes" and "ears" of the car to identify the surrounding environment and vehicles. Then, they can select, analyze, and synthesize the data collected by the arithmetic unit and the control system of the car. In the end, the smart drive is realized through their cooperation.

At present, the common driving assistance systems mainly include the Cruise Control System, the Lane Keeping Assist System, the Auto Parking Assist System, the Brake Assist System, and the Driving Assist System.

3.2.2.1 Cruise Control System

The Cruise Control System (CCS) is a system that can set a fixed speed, keeping the car moving at a constant speed without pressing the gas pedal.

The Adaptive Cruise Control (ACC) system is an advanced version of the CCS. It allows the cruise control system of a car to dynamically adjust its speed to adapt to traffic conditions. The radar installed on the front of the vehicle is able to detect whether a slower vehicle is in the lane ahead of the car. If so, the ACC system will reduce the speed of the car, so that the distance between the two vehicles can be controlled. The system will speed up the vehicle to reach the previously set speed, when it detects the front vehicle is on a different roadway. In this case, the speed can be increased or decreased automatically without driver intervention.

3.2.2.2 Lane Keeping Assist System

The Lane Keeping Assist System can recognize the lane marking lines of the driving lane through cameras to provide support for the vehicle to stay in the lane. The system is on standby, if the marking lines on either side of the lane are detected. The driver can be warned by vibrations in the steering wheel when the vehicle is likely to move out of the lane. Vibrations will not be triggered if the driver wants to change into other lanes, such as turning on the indicator before crossing the marking lines.

3.2.2.3 *Auto Parking Assist System*

The traditional parking system is mainly based on reversing radar and vehicle backup camera telling the driver the relative position between the vehicle and the obstacle in the form of visual image. It also makes a sound to solve the trouble caused by the blind spot in the rearview mirror. Therefore, it is convenient for the driver to reverse and park without any potential safety problems.

In the Auto Parking Assist System, ultrasonic and machine vision are applied for detection. Ultrasonic sensors can detect obstacles and automatically identify the parking line through cameras. When the parking position and distance are detected and the driver presses the confirm key, the system will automatically park the car, then intelligent parking is realized.

3.2.2.4 *Brake Assist System*

The Brake Assist System can distinguish the situation of the driver stepping on the pedal through sensors. Then, it will identify and judge whether to start the emergency brake program. In general, the system will not intervene for the normal brake and drivers decide the force of the brake by themselves. An emergency brake will be triggered if it detects that the driver suddenly presses down on the brake pedal with extreme speed and force. The pressure on the brake system will go up for a higher level of brake pressure. The ideal braking effect can be achieved because the brake assist system can immediately increase the brake pressure to its maximum.

3.2.2.5 *Driving Assist System*

The main functions of the Driving Assist System mainly include super anti-shake video recording, multi-channel synchronous video recording, voice recording, storage, playing, and real-time display. As a result, data can be easily recorded for backup. The operation of the system is user-friendly in driving. Screens can be switched as needed according to the driving state. For instance, only the image recorded by the right camera will be displayed by the LCD if the car turns right. Moreover, the forced switch of screens can be realized with the functions of fast searching and playback.

3.2.3 Smart driving in the 5G era

The situation around can only be detected through on-board sensors, which act as the "eyes" and "ears" of a car during the current stage of smart drive based on a single car. Moreover, road conditions are very complicated. The sensor system of a single car, such as radars, cameras, and laser radars, has limitations because it can be easily affected by environmental factors such as weather and light. There is no way to choose a reasonable route in some unpredictable emergency. As a result, it is very difficult to protect driving safety. Using the technology based on the 5G network, a vehicle–road collaborative system can be established between vehicles and vehicles, vehicles and pedestrians, as well as vehicles and the road network. Having this system is equivalent to knowing "the perspective of a God". With this system, vehicles can detect information from various channels. The environmental information outside the field of vision and the driving intention of nearby vehicles can be timely transmitted to the smart car through the 5G network. In this way, the smart drive can reach the L5 stage, which can make the driving process safer and more convenient.

The 5G network can offer ultra-low latency in milliseconds. Its transmission rate is up to 10 Gb/s, with millions of connections per square kilometer and ultra-high reliability. The communication of information between the car and the external environment in real time can be achieved through the car interconnection technology supported by the 5G network.

V2X refers to the information interaction between vehicles and various external objects. V2X includes the following aspects:

V2I: The communication between vehicles and infrastructure, such as the interaction between the car with traffic lights or intersection signs.
V2V: The vehicle-to-vehicle communication, such as the interaction between cars in intersections or the front and rear vehicles.
V2P: The communication between vehicles and pedestrians, such as the interaction between vehicles and pedestrians crossing the road or cyclists around them.
V2N: The communication between vehicles and the Internet, such as the interaction between the car and the navigation path planning or high-precision maps.

Thanks to V2X, adequate communication between the car and the outside world can be realized to get more information from the outside world. Compared to the smart drive of a single vehicle, the vehicle–road collaborative system of V2X based on the 5G network not only shows vehicle intelligence-oriented focus but also embodies the road wisdom emphasis. Through V2X, roads are connected to cars and the cloud server by the Internet. With this connection, coordinated perception and decision-making can be achieved in aspects of the information between pedestrians, road networks, and cars. In that case, the urban traffic system can truly become a huge V2X. Nowadays, intelligent terminals are connected to the Internet. Likewise, every car is communicating information with pedestrians, vehicles, and road networks, which is equivalent to giving the car a brain with infinite memory to make it competent for more complex computations and endow it with infinite intelligence.

For example, in the scene where a car encounters a stationary vehicle on the road after passing the curve, sensors such as cameras and radars used by the smart drive of a single car cannot detect the danger in advance. Even if a judgment can be made immediately by the car after passing the curve, it is difficult to ensure that no accident will happen. V2X can share information through the Internet, so the moment when the front vehicle stops, it can be detected by other vehicles within a certain range. Therefore, the surrounding vehicles can make decisions in advance so as to avoid accidents.

In addition, the high-precision road navigation map has richer and more detailed road information, which can reflect the real conditions of the road more accurately. Consequently, the amount of data produced is huge. However, it is possible to achieve high-precision navigation with wider data channels and lower data delays offered by the 5G network. With high-precision maps, the navigation in autopilot can be realized. Operations such as environment perception, precise positioning, lane planning, as well as control can be carried out on autopilot through visualization representation of the real scene around. In this way, a three-dimensional world can be displayed to the users, which is more in line with their cognitive habits and it's more comfortable to use these maps with improved autopilot security.

3.2.4 *Smart travel in the 5G era*

5G network is like a key that opens the door of smart transportation in cities in the future. Through the vehicle infrastructure cooperation system, the road will offer the car with its conditions, while the car will provide the road with the collected information. Therefore, cars can collect information from different channels, which can achieve autopilot, safer security, traffic guidance, and road resource allocation with high efficiency.

3.2.4.1 *Autopilot*

(1) *Fully autonomous auto parking*: It is based on the auto parking technology of the vehicle–road collaboration. The intelligent car can automatically drive to the parking lot after the passenger gets off the car, which is shown in Fig. 3.5. During this process, functions such as pedestrian avoidance, vehicle avoidance, and automatic parking lot searching can be fully realized autonomously. Similarly, the passenger can wake up the car to serve him by pressing one button.

(2) *Automatic ride-hailing*: In the future, with the help of 5G and vehicle–road collaboration, passengers can make an appointment to hail a car with their mobile phones. After waiting for a few minutes, a driverless

Figure 3.5 Automatic parking.

Figure 3.6 Automatic ride-hailing.

intelligent car will slowly stop in front of its passenger, which is shown in Fig. 3.6. The car will avoid congested roads according to the automatic planning of the optimal route and take passengers to their destinations, which will alleviate congestion by increasing the usage of cars to reduce the total number of vehicles on the road.

(3) *Remote driving*: In the future, the remote driving technology can be used to reduce the danger coefficient of rescue work and improve the rescue efficiency in special scenes such as disaster relief and road repair. In addition, unmanned precise operations can be realized through remote driving for the production operations in dangerous and harsh environments, such as no man's land, mining areas, and garbage transportation areas. Besides that, multiple cars can be operated by one person. Take another example, in the long-distance transportation industry, the driver can remotely control cars at a fixed working place, which can avoid fatigue driving. Moreover, cars can be driven all day in shifts with higher transportation efficiency.

3.2.4.2 *The protection for pedestrians*

Through the vehicle–road collaboration technology, intelligent vehicles can effectively avoid pedestrians within the visual range. Pedestrians outside the visual range or behind obstacles can also be detected in advance to predict collision risks. In this way, safety risks can be avoided actively, the detection of intelligent cars can be further, blind spots can be detected, and pedestrians will be safer.

3.2.4.3 Traffic safety and efficiency

(1) *Turn auxiliary and intersection game of blind area*: When the intelligent vehicle makes a turn, the road condition is judged by the roadside sensor in an omni-directional manner beyond the visual range with the help of the vehicle–road collaboration technology. Thus, the intelligent vehicle can be guided to pass through the intersection safely without any blind areas. In addition, at intersections without traffic lights, intelligent vehicles can still perceive the conditions of vehicles and pedestrians in all directions at intersections. Collision risks can also be predicted, which can realize road right allocation and autopilot in all road conditions.

(2) *Obstacle identification, avoidance, and intelligent collision avoidance*: Based on the vehicle–road collaboration and the autopilot technology, the intelligent vehicle can automatically identify obstacles to fully realize the avoidance by the brake and driving safety. The core of autopilot technology is the infrastructure communication between vehicles, which allows cars to detect each other and percept roads. Data from other cars can even be shared. For example, a vehicle 300 meters ahead has an emergency brake. With V2X, you will be informed of this situation immediately even if there are three cars between you and that car in front of yours. Serial rear-end collisions can be avoided because cars with two 5G modules will not suffer from the risk of collusion.

(3) *Automatic passage in the construction area*: If it is unable to detect whether the road ahead is under construction in the process of driving, the danger of driving and harming construction personnel will occur. With the vehicle–road collaboration technology, the roadside intelligent devices can detect the road construction conditions. Then, the information is transmitted to the intelligent vehicle to show the construction area ahead. After that, the intelligent vehicle can slow down to pass through the construction area, which can avoid safety accidents and ensure traffic safety.

(4) *In-car display of traffic lights and speed guidance of green wave belt*: Intelligent vehicles and traffic lights can conduct real-time data interaction through the interconnection between vehicles and the road infrastructure. Drivers can directly obtain traffic light information at intersections in their intelligent vehicles. Then, these vehicles can be guided to adjust the speed according to the data of traffic lights,

ensuring smooth passage in the planned path without being hindered by red lights.

(5) *The principle of public transport first*: Through the vehicle–road collaboration technology, this principle can be fully implemented in the special bus lanes in the future. When the vehicle approaches the traffic light, the vehicle will send a signal to the light control system, after which, the red light will automatically turn green to let the bus go ahead.

(6) *Automatic avoidance of special vehicles*: For vehicles such as ambulances, fire trucks, and police cars, time equals the lives of the people when they carry out tasks. Unblocked roads and smooth transportation are the keys to saving lives. Through the vehicle–road collaboration technology, special vehicles can send avoidance signals to the intelligent vehicles ahead in the process of passing. After receiving the signals, the vehicles ahead will select the optimal way of avoidance based on the vehicle–road collaboration technology, thus opening up a passage to save lives and ensure the smooth passing of special vehicles.

(7) *Intelligent speed limit reminder*: Based on the vehicle–road collaboration technology, the RSU can offer the speed limit information to the intelligent car in real time. Compared to the traditional fixed speed limit on the road, the speed limit reminder can flexibly change the speed limit in terms of the actual road conditions. For instance, different speed limits can be set according to the size of traffic flow, so as to dynamically adjust the flow.

(8) *Formation driving*: It is based on the autopilot technology of vehicle–road collaboration and high-precision mapping, which allows the intelligent vehicle to realize low-spacing high-speed automatic formation driving. For each intelligent vehicle in the formation, they can autonomously complete the actions of entering, exiting formation, lane changing, overtaking, and emergency braking. In the process of high-speed driving, a large amount of energy will be consumed by the wind resistance factor. However, the function of driving in formation can minimize the energy consumed by the wind resistance of the following vehicles by making full use of the aerodynamic characteristics, in which case, energy waste can be greatly reduced. Meanwhile, driving in formation can maintain the communication between vehicles and keep the queue driving, thus improving the driving safety and riding experience.

3.3 More Comfortable Travel with the New Forms of Transportation

3.3.1 *Car sharing*

3.3.1.1 *Overview of car sharing*

Car sharing is a product of sharing economy, which means a car is shared by many people. In other words, drivers only have the car use right without ownership. It is similar to renting a car in a short time, which is shown in Fig. 3.7. It's easy to book a car through phones or the Internet. Usually, shared cars are coordinated by companies responsible for issues, such as vehicle insurance and parking. Car sharing can improve the utilization rate of cars, which not only helps users save money but also relieves traffic jams as well as highway wear and tear. Besides, air pollution can be alleviated, with the promising development of car sharing.

3.3.1.2 *History of car sharing*

Car sharing first appeared in the 1940s. It was invented by a Swiss, who organized "Road Trip Cooperatives" around the country. At that time,

Figure 3.7 Shared cars.

after using a car, the driver would hand over its keys to the next person. It was very practical in mountainous countries like Switzerland, where it was easier to set up networks than in flat countries. Countries including Japan and the UK followed suit, but car sharing in these nations never took off. The main reason behind this in Japan was that carmakers did not support the car-sharing scheme. Moreover, the Japanese preferred to own a car of their own. In Britain, despite government support, cheap car rentals hampered the growth of car sharing. With the evolvement of computers, electronic keys, and satellite positioning systems, car sharing is given new meaning besides having the support of the technology. Car sharing can be divided into the following categories:

(1) *Car sharing based on Internet platforms*: "Didi Taxi" is the most typical online car-sharing platform whose biggest characteristic lies in that its shared cars have their special drivers. This platform gathers taxi and private car drivers, so it can offer many services, such as taxi, tailored taxi, carpooling, and chauffeuring. It is the pioneer of car sharing. Given the impetus of the capital, "Didi Taxi" also set up a financial leasing company to expand the car rental business, proceeding into a higher level of the car-sharing ecosystem.
(2) *Traditional car rental mode*: This mode is generally operated by outlets. Having confirmed the needs through telephone, the customer goes to the outlets with valid credentials. Then only after a series of contract signing and the completion of vehicle inspection procedures, the customer is allowed to pick up the car. This model has perfect guarantee measures and cars are in good condition with special maintenance measures. However, the whole process is relatively complex, which makes it difficult to meet the sudden needs of vehicles in high frequency and short distance.
(3) *"On-demand" rental service*: Through the progress of technology and the upgrade of consumption concept, the "on-demand" mode of car sharing has emerged with its main features. Therefore, users can use their mobile phones to autonomously complete the process of car ordering, car picking, door closing, and returning at any time, and the service of car renting is fully unmanned. The total fee paid by consumers in this mode is less than that of online car-hailing. In some cases, the fee is equal to or slightly lower than the price of taking a taxi.

3.3.1.3 *Advantages of car sharing*

The advantages of shared cars are as follows:

(1) *Easy to travel and convenient to use*: The obvious advantage of car sharing is that it makes daily travel easier. In particular, it is a more comfortable way to rent a car for people who haven't yet bought one. You can easily solve travel problems by taking out your mobile phones to look for a shared car, in cases of traffic control issues, business trips with a large amount of luggage, or when not being able to get a taxi.
(2) *Short-term use and cost and time saving*: Compared to users buying their own cars, users only need to pay rent when using shared cars. They don't need to consider issues such as maintenance, daily cleaning, annual car inspection, and parking space purchase, which will cost a lot of time and money. In contrast, car sharing can save both time and cost.
(3) *Alleviated traffic congestion as well as road wear and tear, reduced air pollution, and dependence on traditional energy*: When people are gradually accustomed to using shared cars to travel, the growth of the number of cars on the road can be dramatically reduced. Traffic congestion can be directly eased and road wear and tear can be decreased. At the same time, car sharing can promote the development of new energy vehicles, which will reduce air pollution caused by the exhaust from petrol vehicles and the dependence on traditional energy sources. Therefore, it is more in line with the requirement of intelligent travel.

3.3.1.4 *Disadvantages of car sharing*

Every coin has two sides, and shared cars are no exception. The current disadvantages of shared cars are listed as follows:

(1) *Small scale*: At present, there are a lot of car-sharing enterprises, but they are small in scale with an immature business model. As a result of a lack of management, various expenses, such as initial investment, will be added to the rent, leading to a poor user experience.
(2) *Few shared cars and outlets*: In the early stage of the rise of car sharing in China (2017–2019), many problems emerged, among which the

main problem was the poor user experience caused by few vehicles and outlets. As a consequence, users cannot find places where they can rent cars. In addition, it is well known that shared cars need to be returned to the designated points. However, the number of outlets is small, which makes it convenient to drive but hard to return cars. Counterproductive to the intention of car-sharing emergence, it is not convenient at all. To facilitate users, we first need to increase the distribution of shared cars and the number of outlets. Moreover, problems such as high cost, low profit, difficult supervision, as well as hidden safety dangers should be addressed.

3.3.1.5 Changes in car sharing caused by 5G

What changes will 5G bring to car sharing?

5G can improve the positioning accuracy and timeliness of shared cars to provide a faster way of data exchange between the network and cars. On top of that, AI will also play its role, such as autopilot, autonomous charging, and returning to the maintenance or repair point automatically. In this way, a lot of labor costs can be reduced, such as manual charging and maintenance which includes driving to maintenance or charge and deploying cars at different parking spots.

For users, it is convenient to travel by shared cars. However, they have to go to a designated parking spot every time they pick up the car, which is inconvenient under bad weather conditions, such as rain, snow, and extremely high and low temperature. Today, AI can solve the problem of long distance arising from the lack of shared cars in the nearby parking lot. With AI autopilot, users can make an appointment in advance so that they can use the car after going downstairs, which improves the convenience to use shared cars. In addition, the air conditioner in the car can be turned on in advance according to the user's setting to increase comfort.

3.3.2 *In-vehicle infotainment*

3.3.2.1 Overview of in-vehicle infotainment

The in-vehicle infotainment system (IVI) is an in-vehicle integrated information processing system based on the on-board special CPU, the vehicle bus system, and Internet service. The IVI system coordinates and controls the entire IVI equipment through a specialized on-board processor and an operating system. In this way, users are provided with services such as professional geographic information, multimedia entertainment, and intelligent transportation, which can greatly improve driving safety and comfort. According to different forms of product function, the IVI system can be divided into the information system and entertainment system. The former mainly provides information service for drivers and passengers through equipment, such as navigation engines, software, electronic map, radio broadcast information, and remote communication. The latter provides entertainment services for drivers through compact discs, VCD, radio, and other audio and video equipment. The IVI system can offer online entertainment functions, including three-dimensional navigation, real-time traffic information, network television, auxiliary driving, failure detection, vehicle information, remote working, and wireless communication. It can also provide a series of applications, including the telematics service provider (TSP), which dramatically improves the level of automobile electronics, network, and intelligence.

3.3.2.2 The history of IVI

After more than 100 years of development, a car is no longer a pure transport tool, and it has been developed into a multi-function machine instead of a single-function machine. Similar to the development of cars, the IVI system has also been developed from single to multiple functions.

Faced with the rapid development of IVI, many consumers cannot help but ask questions. What can the IVI system provide? How has the system been developed? What is its future development? Confronted with such questions, we should review the development of the IVI system across various periods as follows:

(1) *The Radio Age*: As an invention that affects the development of mankind, the radio is the earliest IVI equipment. In 1923, cars with radios first appeared in the United States, ushering in the era of automobile entertainment. Although the IVI system has undergone many changes, it is still an indispensable part of the car.
(2) *The Cassette Age*: 1963 was a landmark year when Philips in the Netherlands invented the cassette tape. Not long after the cassette recorder was invented, cars were equipped with cassette retractable dual-purpose machines, which continued until the late 1980s.

(3) *The Digital Age*: Since the technology development brought changes in the 1990s, mankind has entered the digital era. As a result, CD, VCD, and other digital entertainment equipment were invented and IVI equipment also ushered in a period of great development. Particularly in recent years, with the advent of multi-functional integrated products such as DVD (high-density digital video disc), GPS navigation, and Bluetooth, the IVI equipment is also evolving to become more multi-functional, connected, and intelligent for higher-level integration.

(4) *The InkaNet Age*: Connected to the Internet seamlessly, cars have become a mobile information platform, transforming the era from "digitization of individuals" to "networking of groups". Thus, the automobile information age was truly launched.

3.3.2.3 IVI in the 5G era

In addition to high speed, 5G also gave birth to new business models and immersive interactive experience, leading to fundamental changes in video, games, music, advertising, AR/VR, and other industries in the issue. Besides, the distance between content and audience will be greatly shortened. Ultimately, a new and palpable dimension will be added by 5G in the way people entertain themselves. With the advent of the 5G era and the improvement of autonomous driving technology, people are not satisfied with the existing on-board entertainment system. They hope to strengthen visually related on-board entertainment so that they can see as much as possible instead of listening. So, what will be included in IVI in the 5G era? Some of the expected facilities are as follows:

(1) *Communication*: The communication between passengers and cars as well as machines is the first step in IVI. For example, we can use car voice, such as Google's Assistant, AliOS, and BYD DiLink on-board system "XIAODI", gestures, such as the 3D gesture control of BYTON, BMW's gesture control, JUNMA SEEK 5 gesture control, holograph, and on-board robot, or touch to conduct a brief communication with cars, as shown in Fig. 3.8. Of course, these features are already applied in existing vehicles. However, long and seamless conversations are not available now. In addition to the communication between cars and people, the communication between people will also become more convenient. When someone is talking to us, the

Figure 3.8 Communication between people and vehicles.

video image will be displayed on the windscreen, car window, smart surface, and other places in the car with your permission. In this way, it is easier for us to make calls.

(2) *Super cinema*: Watching a movie or listening to a piece of music on a long journey or in a congested road junction, together with appropriate atmosphere lights in the car, will give us more comfort during our boring journey. For example, Audi's 4D cinema and on-board system application in its concept car can turn the window into a screen. so that the car can be changed into a large cinema, which is full of high-tech sense. Daimler's 360° film turns the windscreen into an interactive computer screen, which is similar to IMAX to give you an immersive experience.

(3) *On-board gaming and shopping*: Playing games is another way to spend time during your boring journey. During gaming, the "movement" of the car seats, the wind speed of the air conditioner, the smell of the sweet atmosphere, and the design of the atmosphere lights can be integrated to match the atmosphere of the game, so as to make the experience more real and interesting. You can also have different games to play and customize them by setting parameters. At the same time, we can open shopping apps or a piece of mobile phone software by speaking to the car system. The image of goods will be projected

onto the glass of the car. Such a shopping experience, which will help us to a greater extent, is unprecedented for us.

In the upcoming 5G era, the transmission of information has been accelerated to provide a guarantee for our intelligent travel, thus making our journey more fun rather than a simple connection between the starting and ending points.

> As the communication technology continues to develop, communication tools such as mobile phones have gradually evolved into intelligent terminals. At the same time, remote vehicle control, Big Data early warning, and real-time navigation have been realized due to the application of the new generation of communication technology in V2X. Consequently, we can communicate with the outside world anytime and anywhere, making our travel more convenient and fun. Now, 5G is about to be widely applied. People are looking forward to its application in all industries.
>
> This chapter focuses on the application of 5G in the field of intelligent travel. With the help of 5G, people, cars, roads, environment, and cloud servers can all be connected so that the transportation system can enter the era of intelligent network connection. In this way, comprehensive monitoring, perception, and intelligent decision-making can be achieved at the level of people, cars, roads, and environment. The turning point of the era of intelligent transportation has emerged, accompanied by opportunities within our reach. 5G will lead a new round of technology convergence innovation, fully enabling autonomous driving and smart transportation. With 5G, autopilot with low delay and communication of high reliability and speed can be realized. People, cars, roads, and cloud servers are all connected for coordination. In the era of intelligent traffic network connection, traffic information will be transmitted from unidirectional transmission with management and control to bidirectional transmission. Therefore, service mode innovation can be realized, which will provide users with personalized and customized full-chain services. In the future, the primary task of intelligent transportation is to build an intelligent network transportation system with artificial intelligence and edge computing, causing the transformation from Internet of Everything to intelligent Internet of Everything. In the future, the main development direction of smart transportation is to achieve breakthroughs in relevant technologies.

The application of these technologies should be improved in different complex scenes, which requires the full cooperation of transportation departments, automobile manufacturers, Internet enterprises, and research institutions.

More than 100 years of history of the internal combustion engine era is about to end in the current automobile industry, which is undeniable. The industry will enter a new electric and intelligent era when updating and iteration of technologies will also bring great changes to the whole industrial chain. As the inevitable result of new technologies leads to new business models, services offered by science and technology have been upgraded due to the advent of the 5G era. With the ongoing trend of technological iteration, the automobile industry will also be developed in a more advanced direction.

Chapter 4

Traffic Control with 5G+ — The More Intellectual Management

An efficient transportation system is the key for smart cities to operate well. In the future, the transportation autonomy and interconnection carrying forward will make it imperative to apply advanced interconnection technologies such as 5G not only to vehicles but also to sensors and computer vision systems on roads and sidewalks. Due to the large number of data collected by these devices, real-time processing and analysis are required. Compared to 4G, the connection density will grow by 10 times, the traffic density will rise by 100 times, and the user experience rate of 5G will grow by 10 times with the peak rate of users as well as the delay reaching 10–100 Gb/s and millisecond level, respectively. Thus, 5G is the most reliable network connection technology at present. Transportation departments can apply 5G to real-time road monitoring so as to spot accidents or congestion in time. Meanwhile, Emergency Response Service Departments can calculate the best route to the accident site or medical center by means of 5G so as to strive for the precious time to save lives. Moreover, 5G can create an automatic transportation system featuring unmanned vehicles, automatic signaling, and traffic management, equipping smart cities with safer transportation systems.

Targeted at the current problems such as the demand of crowd migration, passenger flow, cargo flow, and traffic safety, traffic-related data analysis models can be quickly built through technologies such as Big Data, cloud computing, and 5G. These models can realize monitoring and early warning of key stations and road network passenger flow as well as the analysis of crowd travel characteristics, so as to achieve the management goal of traffic controlling, forecasting, and early warning macroscopically and microscopically.

4.1 More Effective Management: One Map of Integrated Information

At present, the transportation industry has accumulated a large number of transportation infrastructure data as well as dynamic collection data of traffic flow, passenger flow, and logistics. Considering such a large number of data, it would be difficult to use it effectively without systematic management, which would restrict the future sustainable development of this industry. An information management platform with an integrated transportation system should be built to step up transformation and upgrading, optimize functions, and conform to the development trend, thus improving the management efficiency.

By introducing advanced technologies such as 5G, GIS, and Big Data, "one information-integrated map" of intelligent transportation and platform applications can be established to realize application functions. Unified data management, auxiliary planning research, project information interaction, road network display, and facility maintenance management are included.

The "one information-integrated map" of traffic can achieve the following goals:

(1) It can integrate data and information resources, build a database of transportation status and comprehensive transportation system planning, and update and maintain effectively in time. Meanwhile, data information is authoritative, presented in real time, and accurate, and the corresponding management authority is set.
(2) It can develop relevant traffic applications, such as traffic Big Data analysis, dynamic display of traffic status, and digital display of traffic planning research results based on traffic-related data.
(3) It can make the linkage among programming, planning, and projects, and promote the transformation of project management from "paper chart" to "dynamic information map". Road monitoring and traffic control play an important part in traffic management, and 5G will give its advantages full play in these two aspects.

4.1.1 *Road surveillance*

4.1.1.1 *Road network operation monitoring*

Urban road network operation monitoring is mainly aimed at monitoring the operation of expressways, national and provincial trunk lines, urban roads, as well as the age and gender of passenger flow. It focuses on real-time monitoring of traffic flow, traffic accidents, and congested sections of urban traffic trunk lines and issues early warnings in time through various channels.

Technologies such as 5G, Big Data, and AI can help monitor the real-time passenger flow, traffic speed, congestion index, and other indicators of road network and important road sections. Early warning threshold can also be set based on other factors such as the specific carrying capacity of urban roads, road environment, meteorological conditions, speed limit, and traffic control. When the detection results exceed the preset threshold, the early warning mechanism will be automatically triggered to achieve rapid warning of the urban road network. An important road section congestion index including congestion duration and congestion distance and interruption events such as traffic accidents is also able to be achieved, as shown in Fig. 4.1.

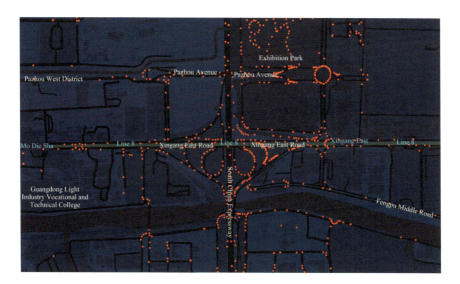

Figure 4.1   Road network operation monitoring.

4.1.1.2 Waterway traffic operation monitoring

5G will accelerate the intellectualization of maritime supervision and waterway traffic management.

First of all, 5G will facilitate the implementation of the sulfur limitation policy. At present, the sulfur limitation policy is implemented by boarding and inspecting selectively whether the ship uses compliant fuel. In the future, the oil consumption and emissions of the ship can be directly detected by data transmission using 5G. In addition, the supervision of the crew on board can be strengthened, so that the specific position of each crew can be tracked at anytime.

Secondly, the operation of waterway transportation can be controlled in real time by means of 5G combined with various data sources, such as inland river shipping data, offshore shipping data, maritime department data, and meteorological data. Therefore, it is possible to promptly monitor the operation status of important inland river and offshore navigation networks as well as important waterway sections. The abnormal incidents of waterway transportation can be spotted and responded to in time to ensure the safety of waterway transportation and improve the efficiency of waterway transportation.

4.1.1.3 Monitoring of major traffic incidents

Monitoring, spotting, notifying, coordinating, and addressing traffic accidents can ensure smooth and safe travel. The main data source of major traffic events is video surveillance. Traffic accidents are monitored, recorded, and forewarned using the 5G edge computing technology. The verified traffic accidents are counted and displayed on the map by classification. When the traffic accidents reach the set level, they will be transferred to the emergency mode, and relevant information will be sent to the Traffic Decision-Making Department for processing and release, as shown in Fig. 4.2.

4.1.1.4 Key monitoring of congested road sections

The traffic flow at traffic nodes, entrances and exits, comprehensive transportation hubs, as well as the surrounding road sections and congested road sections in densely populated areas can be monitored by means of 5G technology. It will be combined with data from transportation enterprise,

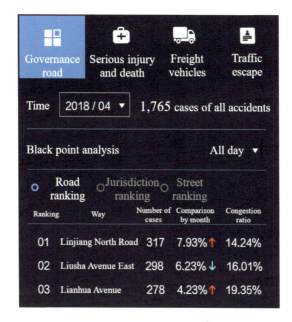

Figure 4.2 Monitoring of major traffic events.

Traffic Control Department, and outfield video. The time and space characteristics such as congested road sections, the speed of congested road sections, and congested duration can be monitored in real time to reflect the traffic conditions of road sections and regions. Early warning threshold can also be set based on other factors such as the specific carrying capacity, geographical environment, meteorological conditions, current and speed limit regulations, and traffic control. When the detection results exceed the preset threshold, the early warning mechanism will be automatically triggered to ease road congestion and resume smooth travel as soon as possible.

4.1.2 *Traffic control*

4.1.2.1 *Adaptive traffic light control based on 5G edge computing*

An intelligent traffic signal control can make the network joint control of all road traffic signal controllers possible. The control center can not only monitor the status and real-time operation information of all road traffic signal controllers but also send remote instructions to the road traffic signal controllers, which is the core of coordination and single-point adaptive control in signal areas. The following aspects can be observed in a control center:

(1) *Traffic signal operation monitoring*: The traffic signal control can monitor the state of the road traffic signal controller. When the road traffic signal controller breaks down or goes offline, the control center gives an alarm in time. At the same time, the control center can monitor the phase, period, and green signal ratio of the road traffic signal controller.
(2) *Signal remote intervention*: When traffic jams or accidents occur at intersections, the control center can remotely regulate the control scheme and signal timing of the road traffic signal controller. As a result, it can remotely operate the traffic signal controller, such as phase locking, parking, phase jumping, timing, flashing yellow lights, and turning off the lights.
(3) *Coordinated control of regional traffic signals*: Bus stations, airports, business districts, hospitals, and other areas are the key areas of the city. Once traffic congestion occurs in these places, the congested area will be enlarged and even be worse, eventually leading to traffic paralysis if traffic guidance is not taken in time. The measures to cope with congestion accidents in key areas include continuous detecting of congestion accidents, analyzing causes, degree of congestion, and the implementation of the regional signal coordination control strategy. Controlling road traffic signals at intersections around the control area can adjust the vehicles entering the control area, thus making them drive into the control area orderly in batches to avoid traffic paralysis.

4.1.2.2 5G intelligent lane control

5G intelligent lane control adopts AI processing technology to collect traffic data in real time, including traffic flow and speed, which are analyzed and processed by AI. Traffic congestion monitoring, real-time adaptive control, bus priority control, and traffic Big Data visualization decision-making can be carried out based on various traffic control requirements. The following features can be implemented:

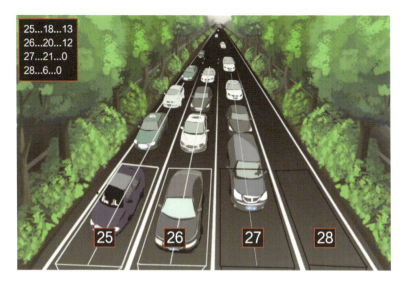

Figure 4.3 Traffic flow monitoring at intersections.

(1) *Monitoring the congestion status of intersection lanes*: An intersection traffic flow detector is set at the intersection to monitor the traffic of the intersection. Inspectors can output indicators reflecting congestion degree such as periodic lane flow, traffic occupancy rate, and traffic saturation at the intersection to visually display the traffic congestion at the intersection, as shown in Fig. 4.3.

Starting with the relationship between queue length and traffic demand, queue length and phase difference, the adaptive control of traffic corridor based on queue length can be used to detect the queue length at the end of red light and green light in each lane of the test intersection. In the signal control algorithm, the phase traffic demand can be reflected by the queue length at the end of the green light and the traffic volume evacuated during the green light. Thus, based on the traffic demand, the green light time of each phase in the signal cycle can be adjusted in time to provide the signal phase matching the traffic demand and traffic capacity for intersections. The phase can be adjusted to realize the self-adaptive optimization of green light time, maximize the vehicle empty capacity, and minimize the empty time. Meanwhile, this algorithm uses the queuing length at the end of the red light and the saturated traffic flow speed during the green light to reflect the evacuation time demand of queuing traffic flow. It implements the real-time optimization of the phase difference between adjacent intersections to provide the phase difference matching the speed of road sections for adjacent intersections. Finally, the phase difference adaptive optimization aiming at non-stop and maximum evacuation capacity can be achieved.

(2) *Real-time adaptive control*: The road traffic signal controller in the control area operates on the network with the regional control computer. The signal timing scheme is generated by the system optimization algorithm software in real time based on the actual traffic conditions, which can be downloaded by the road traffic signal controller to the executive. The actual traffic situation is mainly obtained by analyzing basic traffic data such as lane flow and occupancy rate obtained by road traffic information collection equipment (video detector).

(3) *Bus priority control*: Bus signal priority is being attached great significance in urban traffic development. The road traffic signal control platform can help the road traffic signal controller perceive the bus by intelligent means, learn the travel demand of buses deeply, and automatically adopt the signal control methods such as extending green light, shortening red light and interspersed phase to give priority to the bus, and display the priority information of the bus on the intersection screen.

(4) *Visual decision-making of traffic Big Data*: Various traffic control modes can be set through the visual analysis of traffic Big Data. The road traffic signal controller can execute corresponding control schemes at different time periods based on the pre-signal timing scheme to control the road traffic signal lights.

4.1.2.3 *Command and dispatch*

With the aid of Big Data decision-making, when emergency vehicles such as fire engines, ambulances, and emergency vehicles pass the road, the signal lights can be pushed by green waves according to the predetermined route. Therefore, the emergency vehicles are unimpeded, and illegal vehicles can be intercepted by red lights. The following features can be implemented:

(1) *Emergency vehicle life channel*: Police cars, fire engines, ambulances, and other emergency vehicles are key to urban emergency rescue.

Under special circumstances, rescue support roads can be dynamically planned, and appropriate intersection signal timing can be given priority based on the needs of emergency vehicles. Thus, the shortest rescue path can be delivered to emergency vehicles, while the queue length can be cleared in advance. The rapid passage of emergency vehicles can be guaranteed with minimum traffic interference. The road traffic signal control platform can set corresponding guarantee routes and channels to ensure that special service vehicles carrying out special service tasks meet all green lights all the way. At the same time, the safety of such vehicles can also be ensured by video surveillance.

(2) *Red light interception of vehicles violating traffic rules*: The key controlled vehicles in the city, including vehicles violating traffic rules many times, vehicles escaping from the accident, drunk driving, drug driving, and other vehicles that need accurate control, are the targets of the relevant departments to track and investigate. The key vehicles can be accurately deployed and controlled based on specific needs using Big Data to assist decision-making. At the same time, red light interception of vehicles can be operated with the aid of surrounding signal lights so that the vehicles under investigation and control can by no means escape, as shown in Fig. 4.4.

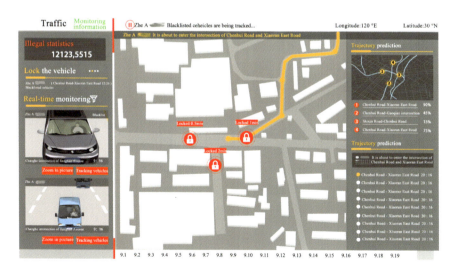

Figure 4.4 Red light interception of illegal vehicles.

4.1.2.4 Information release

The traffic signal control system is the control center of road traffic signal controllers, which is the most direct and the most basic application system in urban traffic signal control. The road traffic operation efficiency can be fully guaranteed mainly through the networking and joint control of urban road traffic signal controllers. With the advent of the Internet of Things, artificial intelligence, and Big Data era, many "data islands" have been broken down and road traffic signal control has also transformed from the traditional and independent chimney architecture to the "Internet plus traffic signal control" era. The following features can be implemented:

(1) *Mobile phone terminal*: The mobile phone terminal relies on communication operators' Big Data location tags and the short message group sending to make the accurate push of short messages possible. The permanent users and roaming users in the designated area can be comprehensively analyzed by means of base station coverage and Big Data technology. It can establish a real-time dynamic data model and lock the users staying near the designated area within the time limit as well as deliver short traffic messages to users.

(2) *Large screen at the intersection*: Large screens at intersections are mainly used for road monitoring and commands at various intersections, including assisting traffic police to ease traffic, allocating monitoring resources at intersections, controlling traffic lights, and road rescue. Traffic management personnel can not only have a comprehensive idea of the road traffic of the whole city without leaving the control center but also release information in real time to make traffic smoother, as shown in Fig. 4.5.

4.2 More Intellectual Allocation for Urban Traffic Network

Gone are the days when people had difficulty in traveling. Now, the roads are connected with each other, so traveling is much easier. We are witnessing the rapid development of the city all the time. Customized applications can be targeted based on diversified application scenarios such as public transportation, taxis, rail transit (rail transit), and stations with the innovative technology of 5G.

Figure 4.5 Large screen at the intersection.

4.2.1 *Smart bus*

4.2.1.1 *Bus route optimization*

Based on the location data of mobile phone users of communication operators, the daily travel data of bus passengers can be analyzed, including origin–destination (OD) point analysis, travel route analysis, travel distance analysis, and transfer station analysis, as shown in Fig. 4.6.

Based on the above analysis, the smart bus can optimize routes. For example, based on the number of passengers and the travel time distribution of each bus line, the operational efficiency and reasons for the low operational efficiency of each bus line can be analyzed, thus putting forward optimization suggestions. The bus shifts can be increased for the high rank of buses in the number of passengers of peak hours. The bus route can be optimized by considering some factors, such as potential bus users, existing bus passengers, the service range of stations and routes, road grade, and total distance of routes.

4.2.1.2 *Bus stop planning*

On the basis of route planning, bus stops can be planned reasonably by taking some factors into consideration, such as gathering areas, workplaces and leisure places, as well as the distance between bus stops.

100   *The World of 5G: Intelligent Transportation*

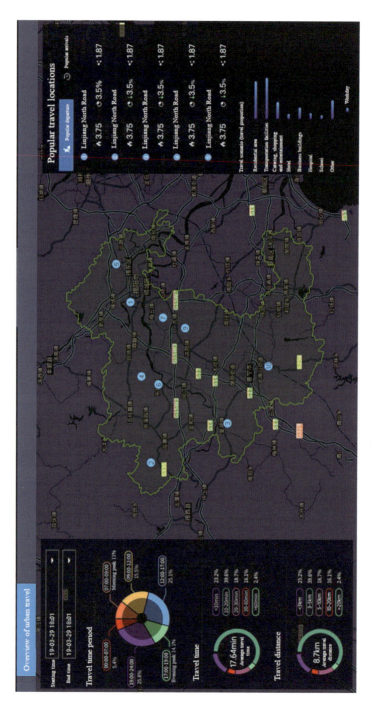

Figure 4.6   Overview of urban travel.

4.2.1.3 *Traffic pressure analysis of existing bus stops*

The number of passengers in each bus stop can be analyzed, and the instantaneous traffic pressure of a bus stop can be studied based on the time distribution. Stations with high traffic pressure can be optimized by increasing bus shifts or adjusting other adjacent lines to the station to relieve the traffic pressure of the station.

4.2.1.4 *Traffic analysis around large residential areas*

By analyzing the traffic flow around each large residential area, the location concentration of bus passengers in these surrounding areas, the location distribution of existing bus stops around, and the urgency of these passengers' bus ride demand, the location of nearby bus stops can be adjusted reasonably. At the same time, new bus stops can be added to solve the inconvenient traveling problems for residents in large residential areas and nearby residents.

In addition, the traffic conditions around important areas such as large-scale office places, large-scale activity places, and shopping malls can be analyzed. The station needs of bus passengers in these important places can be studied to appropriately optimize old stations or add new stations, thus meeting the travel needs of bus passengers.

4.2.2 Smart rail transit

4.2.2.1 *Forecast the future passenger flow*

It is well known that the higher the frequency of the signal, the worse the diffraction ability will be and the greater the loss will be. Similarly, the farther the distance, the greater the loss will be. Compared to 4G, the frequency band of 5G is higher than 4G. The coverage of the 5G base station will be smaller than that of the 4G base station. Therefore, if other factors are not taken into consideration, the density of the 5G base station must be much higher than that of 4G, so that the accuracy of positioning based on the base station will be greatly improved to achieve the same coverage effect.

Based on the positioning of 5G base station, we can more accurately monitor the passenger flow information of rail transit and the passenger flow data of core transfer stations in real time as well as analyze and forecast based on previous data, which can accurately predict the passenger flow situation in the future. Thus, decision makers can make more targeted work plans and organize operations more effectively. They can also start the passenger flow emergency management plan in advance if necessary, such as notifying passengers to change the bus route in advance.

4.2.2.2 AR glasses handling emergencies

AR glasses technology is still in its initial stage. In the 4G era, because the transmission rate is not fast enough to solve the problem of signal delay, people will have nausea and dizziness after wearing AR glasses. High speed and low delay of 5G can provide a smooth and non-stuck experience for video transmission after 5G is put into use.

In the 5G era, subway managers will wear advanced "high-tech" equipment. For example, station attendants can synchronize the situation in place in real time by means of positioning bracelets. The station attendant can communicate with the command room visually by means of the mobile terminal. The blind spots of existing video surveillance can be effectively made up for by deploying more mobile cameras. Commanders can guide station attendants to deal with emergencies from the first perspective by means of AR glasses. In addition, it can remotely troubleshoot based on AR technology and make efficient operation and maintenance possible.

4.2.2.3 Transforming 5G into Wi-Fi high-speed Internet access

Transforming the 5G network into a Wi-Fi hotspot breaks the equipment barrier of the 5G network. Passengers can experience the high speed and smoothness of the 5G network on rail transit without changing their mobile phones, making it faster to scan code and get in and out of the station.

4.2.3 Smart stops and stations

The ability of real-time return of 5G remote video and high-precision positioning will provide strong support for the construction of smart stations. In the future, scenes such as high-definition video surveillance, face recognition, early warning of flow, emergency monitoring, and navigation robots will be gradually added to the smart station, thus enhancing the intelligence and security of the station.

4.2.3.1 Smart parking management

At present, the primary problem in the development of major cities is the difficulty of parking. There are four main reasons for the difficulty of parking: (1) big shortage in parking space; (2) low parking space utilization rate; (3) difficulty in parking; (4) weak parking lot management. How to effectively improve the utilization rate of parking spaces, add parking guidance, strengthen the intelligent management of parking lots, and make "parking freedom" possible are the key problems to be solved urgently in urban management.

The "end–edge–cloud" hierarchical architecture can be constructed through the 5G holistic program of edge-to-cloud collaboration. By making a collaboration of resources, data, and services between the edge and the cloud, the efficiency of business flow processing can be rapidly improved. The data processing load in the cloud can be effectively relieved, thus reducing the data transmission delay to a great extent. The parking lot 5G cloud control center, an integral part of the 5G network edge cloud collaboration system, can flexibly complete a series of operations including on-site independent scheduling, inter-site information collaboration, and off-site auxiliary guidance.

5G communication can integrate 5G signals, vision, and other multi-source heterogeneous positioning perception information sources and finally generate the precise location of vehicles. The real-time positions of vehicles to be parked, other vehicles, and pedestrians in the parking lot can be accurately identified by fusion positioning technology which provides safety tips to avoid congestion and collision in the parking lot.

The 5G cloud control center can acquire the traffic situation based on the parking space allocation result and collect the solid-state information, movement information, and real-time road condition information of vehicles in combination with multi-source sensing equipment in the field. The collected information can be uploaded to the 5G cloud control center and then be integrated and analyzed to provide driving route suggestions for vehicles. Then, the cloud control center can generate real-time navigation, deliver the information to the mobile phone terminal or the parking lot display screen, thus guiding the vehicle to the parking space.

In addition, the parking data of parking lots at all levels can be collected through wireless networks like 5G without gap coverage. After they are integrated in a unified way in real time to the comprehensive management center and processed by the database, effective, timely, and comprehensive reference and guidance decision data can be formed, providing information such as parking remote supervision, data statistical analysis and display, as well as decision-support analysis for business units and drivers. At the same time, it can provide multi-channel bus information services for the public, that is, the public can inquire about the bus operation status through smartphones to plan their own trips.

4.2.3.2 Smart travel

The tourism Big Data platform can deliver information to the mobile phones of passengers who have purchased their travel tickets one hour or half a day in advance.

At the station entrance, 5G facial recognition equipment can be added to identify passengers, obtain the identity information of passengers in video surveillance, as well as count and analyze the passengers who have purchased the tickets.

It can provide comprehensive query and statistics of passenger information, including query and statistics of their basic information and record information of passengers entering and leaving stations. In addition, it can also provide analysis such as key passenger identification.

Intelligent ticket checking equipment can be set at the check-in gate, which supports intelligent automatic ticket checking by means of ID card and QR code, making fast and convenient ticket checking possible.

In addition, Big Data analysis can also be carried out on passenger flow, such as statistical analysis of current total number, source and length of stay of people, and other data of passenger flow in the station area. It can perform a comprehensive analysis of passengers' sex, age, occupation, and industry to provide relevant service guidance for passengers after arriving at their destination, as shown in Fig. 4.7.

4.2.3.3 Station security

The station security system is equipped with the personnel identification function. When strangers or personnel on the control list are detected, it will automatically send out early warning information to remind the

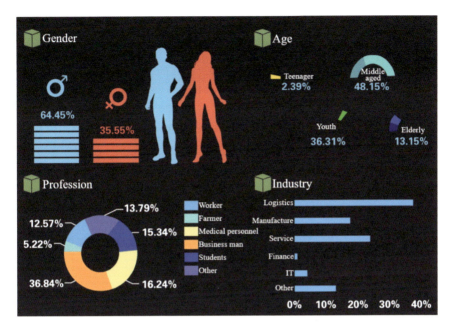

Figure 4.7   Passenger flow portrait.

relevant personnel on duty. Meanwhile, it records the on-site movement information of the person, which is convenient for subsequent tracking and record inquiry.

The system is also equipped with the comprehensive information statistics function, including the query statistics of personnel's basic information, strangers' early warning records, as well as personnel's entering and leaving records. As a result, the security and management can be strengthened.

The system can also carry out portrait retrieval based on the captured portraits by cameras deployed at various positions. After integrating the deployment position information, it can form the activity track information of a certain person at anytime in the region, which can be used to help find and fix the position of strangers.

Infrared cameras can be installed around the station yard. When external objects or people appear, the cameras can be automatically induced to record and warn in real time. The electronic screen on the perimeter can show the specific alarm position. Then, the personnel on duty can immediately notify the mobile security guards to dispatch for handling, which can effectively prevent illegal invasion.

4.2.3.4 Face recognition in stations

So far, most passenger transport has adopted the real-name ticket purchase with ID card. However, testing whether the passenger and ID card can be matched depends on the manual check of ticket inspectors, which is time-consuming, inefficient, and error-prone. To ensure the safety of passengers, prevent, and eliminate the phenomenon that the passenger cannot be matched with the ID card, it is necessary to further introduce face recognition AI technology and improve the intelligent management level of passenger stations to ensure that passenger, ID card, and ticket can be matched.

Facial recognition technology can be applied in many aspects, such as ticket selling, ticket taking, face scanning, and ticket checking.

During the process of ticket selling in passenger stations, the ticket seller can carry out the real-name authentication after confirming the passengers' travel time and bus information. Then, the passenger can put the ID card on the person-to-card comparison machine to carry out real-name authentication. If it turns out to be right, the result can be returned to the ticket seller so that the tickets can be sold. Passengers can also choose their own bus shift on the automatic machine based on their needs. After they choose the bus shift, they can carry out the real-name authentication by face scanning. If the authentication turns out to be right, the result will be transmitted to the ticket terminal and the ticket can be printed through the printer. It can also send a QR code or a link short message directly to the passenger's mobile phone according to the instruction.

During the process of ticket taking in the passenger station, if passengers buy tickets through online channels (such as app or webpage) or purchase the tickets through other people, they need to go to the ticket collection office to complete the real-name authentication with an ID card or through the non-license method. If the authentication turns out to be right, the result will be transmitted to the ticket terminal and the ticket can be printed through the printer.

During the process of face scanning and ticket checking, ID card information can be delivered to the entrance guard at the front end corresponding to the ticket gate in batches based on the train number, and a specific time can be set as the allowed ticket checking time (e.g., 20 min before the car starts). During the process of ticket checking, passengers are required to show their personal ID cards, and the network comparison can be carried out through the near-field communication (NFC) ID card

Figure 4.8 Face recognition for access control.

identification module. When passengers pass at the specified entrance guard and at the specified time, "purchased tickets" will be displayed on the entrance guard screen and face scanning will be carried out at the same time to check whether the passenger and the ID card can be matched. If it turns out to be right, passengers can pass the gate, as shown in Fig. 4.8.

4.3 Smoother Transport for Long-distance Passenger and Freight Service with 5G

After years of continuous construction, optimization, and adjustment by communication operators, the activity spaces of most people are basically covered by mobile signals with few blind spots. By mapping the mobile signal data of mobile phone users' time series to the real geographical position, the spatial activity track of mobile phone users can be completely and objectively restored. Therefore, the population spatial distribution and activity characteristic information can be discovered.

Big Data is characterized by a large number of users and wide scene coverage. These characters fully meet the requirements of precise location, deep portrait of users, and real-time data transmission in intelligent traffic analysis, laying a data foundation for the application and development of intelligent traffic.

People, vehicles, and roads can be fully integrated through the combination of mobile Internet data and traffic data, which truly reflects traffic conditions and makes urban traffic smarter.

4.3.1 *Smart port*

As the hub of modern transportation, ports play an important role in international trade. According to relevant statistics, about 90% of global trade is carried out by the shipping industry. Efficiency is the key in port operations. Traditional ports rely heavily on manpower to operate container cranes at the near end. Due to the harsh working environment, high labor intensity, and shortage of manpower, traditional ports can no longer meet the needs of the rapid development of global shipping. Global ports are generally in pursuit of port automation and intelligent construction.

Intelligentization has become an important goal of port construction. Remote control of port machines, unmanned driving of port vehicles, and port video surveillance + AI management will become an important part of intelligent ports, which require huge network bandwidth support. The reconstruction of the original port network lines is very costly. 5G, featuring high speed and wide connection, can solve the insufficient bandwidth problem of the original network lines in smart port construction.

4.3.1.1 *Remote control of port machine*

With the rapid growth of 5G, a brand new communication scheme is provided for port construction machinery, and 5G injects new impetus into port intelligent construction using its technical advantages of high speed, low delay, and high reliability. According to years of practical experience, improving the efficiency of container transshipment is the core demand of the port, and the remote control of tire cranes is the priority scenario. The real-time return of HD video of tire crane can be made possible because of the high-speed capability of 5G. Likewise, remote real-time control can be made possible because of the low-delay capability of 5G. Container operators can not only carry out the operations such as precise movement and container grabbing in the central control room but also control multiple tire cranes, thus improving the working environment and efficiency.

4.3.1.2 *Unmanned driving of port vehicles*

5G can not only provide convenient and low-cost wireless network connection for various applications such as unmanned driving of port vehicles but also combine edged computing + AI capabilities to help port equipment synchronize and coordinate production, so the efficiency and intelligent operation level of port operations will rise.

4.3.1.3 *Port video surveillance + AI*

A large-scale three-dimensional monitoring mode which monitors the port both entirely and partly can be realized by building a "smart port" based on 5G + MEC. AR panoramic cameras can remotely acquire the real-time full-motion video of the port area by building an AR real-time command platform, so it is convenient for production dispatchers to conduct realtime command of operation lines and adjust the operation mode. AR real-time command has become an advanced means of operation command in the port area.

The high-definition surveillance camera installed in the cab of the harbor bridge can quickly transmit the real-time video of the cab to the MEC server through 5G. The facial expression and driving state of the driver can be intelligently analyzed through the real-time video. Once the driver has an unusual condition such as being tired or dozing off, the MEC server will immediately send out early warning information. 5G solves insufficient bandwidth and prolonged time in the 4K ultra-high-definition video surveillance scene, which provides clearer video images and improves the efficiency of intelligent analysis and real-time response speed. Accordingly, the accident rate of port production is lowered, and the safety of port operations and drivers' lives is ensured.

Due to the 5G + MEC edge cloud computing technology and the high bandwidth of 5G, real-time high-definition images taken by mobile devices carried by transfer vehicles and personnel can be transmitted to the existing AR server in the future port area to further refine the production command. At the same time, the 5G + MEC edge cloud computing technical scheme will lay a foundation for automatic driving, remote control, active early warning, and intelligent security. It is helpful to comprehensively promote the automation and intelligence level of the port area.

4.3.2 *Smart airport*

The smart airport service system comprehensively applies the latest technology of "5G + AI", redefining the new standards of intelligent, scene-oriented, and convenient aviation services. It brings an unprecedented smart travel experience to passengers.

Based on the whole process of air travel, the system builds a three-dimensional intelligent travel service, "walking around the airport with one face", "intelligent experience by one network", and "baggage control with one core", which brings about infinite possibilities for air intelligent travel.

4.3.2.1 Walking around the airport only with customer's face

With the application of new technologies such as 5G and AR glasses in civil aviation, systems such as check-in by face scanning and facial recognition at the engine room entrance can be introduced to make it possible to finish the whole process, from ticket purchase to check-in. By face scanning, passengers can complete various travel processes such as ticket purchase, check-in, luggage check-in, security check, and boarding. The facial recognition system at the entrance can carry out passenger reinspection, inventory, confirmation, and seat guidance. The service accuracy can be promoted effectively and let passengers feel the ease and convenience of smart travel.

4.3.2.2 Intelligent experience by one net

The comprehensive coverage scheme of macro base station, micro base station, and digital room can be adopted to realize the all-round network coverage of airport terminal building, corridor area, flight area, and airline base.

With the continuous development of 5G services and the landing deployment of more innovative 5G applications, apps can be used to intelligently deliver service information in the whole process. Worries for passengers can be removed in pre-trip, in-trip, post-trip, and flight changes. In addition, innovative applications such as ultra-high-definition multi-channel video backhaul can provide passengers with visual, scene-oriented, immersive, and interactive travel experiences, making passengers feel the charm of aviation services in the 5G era.

4.3.2.3 Baggage control with one core

The 5G baggage tracking project can visualize the whole baggage transportation process while passengers can check the status of checked baggage at anytime. At that time, passengers can apply for a permanent electronic luggage tag through the app. The electronic tag adopts a "passive" design with an embedded Radio Frequency Identification (RFID) chip, which can accurately track the baggage position and make the baggage "traceable" throughout the whole process. After completing the self-service check-in in the app, passengers can choose baggage check-in. By putting the electronic baggage tag close to the mobile phone for data sensing, the flight number, baggage destination, and other information can be input in a few seconds. After that, passengers can complete baggage delivery by activation in the counter, thus making the whole process of paperless possible. Compared to traditional counter handling, "passive" electronic luggage tags make travel smarter and more convenient. The ground service staff can also query passengers' luggage quickly in real time, thus improving the baggage handling efficiency.

4.3.3 *Smart train/bus station*

The smart station can realize indoor and outdoor positioning, passenger flow trajectory, ticketing data, and real-time monitoring by using the new room base station Big Data platform. It provides a valuable reference for passenger flow analysis, emergency management, commercial value analysis of waiting hall, and accurate advertising.

In the 5G era, it is inevitable to upgrade traditional stations into smart ones. With the development of 5G, there will be more applications of the construction of smart stations.

After the completion of smart stations, the high-speed network coverage will come true. The video cameras control in the station will be changed from fixed-point installation to mobile cameras. Station inspectors can transmit high-definition videos to the servers at anytime, realizing the station mobile deployment. The food delivery robot in the restaurant in the station can accurately locate through the 5G network, thus delivering food to passengers accurately. VR head-mounted display (virtual reality head-mounted display device) with local characteristics can be deployed in the station. Passengers who don't have time to go to local scenic spots can appreciate the beautiful scenery through the VR heads placed in the station, which can add some fun to the tiring journey.

The construction of smart station is being developed and the coverage of 5G network will promise it wider application space. The smart station will show the wisdom of railway science and technology to the public from railway construction and operation to railway service, ushering in the intelligent era of railway. From wireless Wi-Fi to enter into a station by facial recognition, from intelligent robot navigation to "smart toilet", the increasingly intelligent railway can bring a smoother travel and a better life for passengers. This is also one of the concrete manifestations of science and technology changing society. Smart stations with 5G will actually change people's lives.

4.3.4 The supervision on two types of passenger vehicles and vehicle for explosive terms

In recent years, the number of vehicles operated by *"two types of passenger vehicles and vehicle for explosive terms"* (chartered cars engaged in tourism, route buses with class above three, and vehicles for dangerous goods transport) has surged. Traffic safety accidents of these vehicles account for a considerable proportion of the total number of traffic accidents. In particular, serious traffic accidents with mass casualties, huge economic losses, and extremely bad influence are mostly related to these vehicles. Therefore, it is necessary to improve the efficiency of road transport safety management. At present, China's road transport safety management method is single, which relies too much on manpower. In this case, "two types of passenger vehicles and vehicle for explosive terms" cannot be supervised or continuously supervised when running on the road. Serious illegal operations will happen, for example, overcrowding, overloading, fatigue driving, speeding, and vehicles for dangerous goods transport not driving according to the scheduled route. Such a static means of supervision is not suitable for the rapid development of road traffic. Therefore, how to use modern information means to strengthen the dynamic supervision of "two types of passenger vehicles and vehicle for explosive terms" is particularly critical.

Real-time data (position, speed, and direction) of vehicle running state can be obtained by 5G transmission and position monitoring technology, which can be transmitted to the control center through the wireless communication network. At the same time, the control center can also send back the detected alarm or early warning information such as misoperation or potential safety hazard to the driver in time. At the same time, real-time information will be fed back interactively between entities through the network, thus effectively preventing the safety accidents of "two types of passenger vehicles and vehicle for explosive terms".

The 5G transceiver can be installed at the terminal of the "two types of passenger vehicles and vehicle for explosive terms" operating the vehicle to realize the functions of vehicle positioning. The communication module can be installed to make it possible for "two types of passenger vehicles and vehicle for explosive terms" and the monitoring center to exchange voice, video, and data. At the same time, all kinds of sensors and controllers can be installed to make it possible to collect the signals of these vehicles and give an alarm. Real-time monitoring of vehicles, audio and video scheduling, safety analysis, and management can be completed in the monitoring center to release real-time information and accident emergency alarms. In case of accident, danger, or other emergencies of *two types of passenger vehicles and vehicle for explosive terms*, staff in the monitoring center can obtain the on-site situation and inform relevant departments in time based on the actual danger level. The emergency rescue center and other departments can handle the emergency of these vehicles in time. Therefore, the following functions can be realized: (1) various monitoring methods such as real-time tracking or intermittent tracking to monitor the status of "two types of passenger vehicles and vehicle for explosive terms", drivers, and road environment; (2) multi-vehicle, sub-regional, and cross-regional monitoring; (3) the information exchange of voice, data, and image between the monitoring center and the vehicle-mounted terminal equipment and related personnel; (4) functions such as vehicle dispatching command, safety analysis and management, accident prediction, and early warning.

4.3.5 *Smart logistics*

Compared to the development of the foreign logistics industry, the domestic logistics industry is still in the developing stage. With the continuous improvement of transportation and communication infrastructure, basic logistics facilities are no longer the bottleneck restricting the development of the industry. Among logistics enterprises, transportation and storage are two parts with a relatively high cost, which also happens to be the main gap between domestic logistics enterprises and foreign counterparts. 5G provides new ideas and new ways for domestic logistics enterprises to make up for shortcomings.

4.3.5.1 Intelligent warehousing

After the advent of 5G, the development of Internet of Things will also bring new changes to intelligent warehousing. Warehousing enterprises can not only realize full-automatic warehousing but also reasonably control the import and export of goods.

Full-automatic warehousing will reduce a large number of labor costs for enterprises and greatly improve the warehousing operation and maintenance efficiency of enterprises. Through the three-dimensional automatic warehousing system, warehousing enterprises can integrate light, machinery, electricity, and information for management and control. Therefore, integrated management of material transmission, identification, sorting, stacking, warehousing, retrieval, and sale can be carried out.

In addition to the full-automatic warehousing, enterprises can also grasp the storage of goods through Big Data. Of course, the demand distribution of goods in different regions can also be inferred through data analysis, so that the flow of goods with "destinations" comes true.

Taking a logistics enterprise as an example, first of all, by analyzing shopping habits and purchasing power of users, Big Data can predict the goods with strong purchasing power of users in a certain area. Then, it can send the goods to the designated front warehouse through the logistics system. After the customer places an order, the automatic warehousing system of the front warehouse can start sorting and delivery. When the courier arrives at the warehouse, the goods will be already waiting for delivery at the delivery port, which dramatically improves the efficiency of warehousing and reduces the redundancy and loss of warehousing.

4.3.5.2 Smart distribution

In addition to warehousing, transportation costs also account for a large proportion of logistics costs, so the effective control of transportation costs is of great significance in reducing the total logistics costs. Distribution is a key link in the whole transportation process. During the process of transportation and distribution, getting through the "last kilometer" is the difficulty and pain spot for every logistics enterprise.

With the advent of the 5G era, unmanned aerial vehicles and unmanned vehicles will bring great convenience to the "last kilometer" of logistics, as shown in Fig. 4.9. Unmanned aerial vehicle distribution services and unmanned express delivery vehicles can reduce cost

Figure 4.9 Drone delivery.

effectively at the end of logistics. In addition, besides reducing labor costs, intelligent transportation can also optimize vehicle scheduling and transportation routes, thus improving the on-time delivery rate.

In addition to unmanned driving, real-time monitoring of vehicles is also very important. 5G will improve the communication ability of vehicles in an all-round way, so that logistics enterprises can trace and manage vehicles on the basis of vehicle networking.

4.4 Accident Prevention and Emergency Response

4.4.1 *Management of transportation accidents*

Road traffic accident is a major public safety problem, which ranks eighth in the leading cause of death in the world. The total number of road traffic accidents, the death rate per 10,000 vehicles, and the ratio of death and injury due to traffic accidents in China are all higher than those in developed countries. Traffic accidents not only bring huge losses to individuals, families, and society but also bring heavy burdens to the national or regional economy. It has become one of the important factors that endanger the safety of people's lives and property in China, affecting social harmony and stability. In order to reduce casualties and economic losses caused by traffic accidents and improve the efficiency of road traffic management, traffic accident information management is an inevitable trend. With the development and innovation of information technology, the probability of accidents can be predicted by accurately analyzing the causes of accidents with a large amount of accumulated data and scientific analysis methods. The formulation of policies, such as the regulation of accident-prone road sections is guided. These analysis methods can analyze the accurate causes of traffic accidents, with small investment and great results, thus formulating targeted countermeasures to reduce the incidence of traffic accidents.

To prevent traffic accidents, Big Data technology can be used to develop traffic accident early warning systems. Based on the collected massive data, early warning mechanisms at macro, meso, and micro levels can also be established with different analysis methods used for analysis and rapid judgment. As long as road sections with major potential safety hazards can be inquired, the association analysis can be carried out based on space and time. It assists the traffic police to quickly carry out multi-level macro-security judgment. For example, the accident and traffic violation data can be displayed on the map and the spatial distribution characteristics of accidents and law enforcement can be explored through accident and traffic violation analysis. Frontline police should be instructed to strengthen law enforcement in the road sections with high accident and traffic violation frequency.

Law enforcement means can also be innovated through Big Data, that is, one is investigating and punishing illegal honking. The sound electronic eye that can realize sound source positioning through microphone array technology can accurately identify honking vehicles in dense vehicles. Another is targeted at vehicles which do not give way to pedestrians and turn without giving way to vehicles going straight. Electronic police video combined with photos can be used to analyze their tracks and identify traffic violation vehicles, thus doing an investigation and choosing a punishment.

Traffic Control with 5G+ — The More Intellectual Management 117

Figure 4.10 Face recognition captures pedestrians running red lights.

Facial recognition and biometric technology can be used to identify and punish pedestrians running red lights, as shown in Fig. 4.10.

In addition, for fraudulent traffic accidents commonly known as "accident fraud", the ID number and vehicle number can be counted and the frequency of its occurrence in the accident area can be analyzed. If it occurs continuously, further relevant criminal investigation analysis can be carried out.

4.4.2 *Safety and emergency*

Nowadays, with the rapid development of the economy, transportation has become an indispensable part of people's life. When it comes to common problems of urban traffic, many people may be suffering from it. During the rush hour, traffic congestion caused by objective factors such as road repair, traffic control, and signal lamp failure as well as traffic accidents such as vehicle collisions and injuries to people and objects often caused great suffering.

Traffic emergency is an important part of the urban emergency command system. Traffic congestion, frequent traffic accidents, and traffic pollution have had serious impacts on urban operations and residents' lives. The emergency management of urban traffic urgently needs a real-time, accurate, and efficient visual monitoring mechanism which can obtain the traffic operation at anytime, such as where did the traffic accident happen? Where is the traffic jam? Which section is the smoothest? and so on to help the traffic management departments improve their ability of emergency command and decision-making.

With the advent of the 5G era, traffic safety emergencies will usher in a new round of innovation and upgrading. As we all know, the advantages of 5G mainly include faster transmission rate, shorter delay, and larger number of connections. In terms of traffic emergencies, 5G can transmit the data collected by various sensors and cameras faster, which is the important basis of decision analysis.

How does the information platform based on 5G, Big Data, and AI provide intelligent decision support for emergency command in transportation?

Early warning and warning support can be provided for emergencies such as natural disasters, accidents, public health events, social security events, and major events that may affect the normal operation of traffic as well as traffic peak hours and traffic conflicts. To cope with large-scale activities, special missions, bad weather, and daily congestion in key areas, relevant emergency plans can be established. At the same time, relevant elements and command processes of the plans can be visually presented in various ways and deployed through the platform, so as to improve the familiarity of traffic commanders and duty personnel with the plans as well as enhance their ability to handle emergencies. Meanwhile, it is necessary to integrate the relevant resources needed for traffic safety supervision and emergency support through the platform. Thus, the information management of the resources related to emergency command can be made possible. The command and invocation of relevant personnel, materials, technology, and equipment by commanders under emergency conditions can be facilitated. All linkage departments can be coordinated to carry out the prevention and disposal of emergencies in advance.

In an emergency state, emergency personnel can quickly inquire about the relevant information of emergency events through the information platform. It is convenient for commanders to judge and analyze the location and surrounding conditions of the police as well as carry out operations, such as deployment, resource allocation, and order issuing. It can strengthen the flat command and dispatch ability of the command center and enhance the ability of the command center to deal with emergencies. In order to provide powerful data support for traffic management departments to conduct early warning, routine analysis, and thematic judgment, it is necessary to analyze, summarize, and integrate the processing data of historical major traffic events. Thus, the data will be scientific and reliable, and decision support for traffic special key governance work can be offered.

The transportation industry is a large and complex system, which bears tremendous pressure in emergencies, such as accidents, natural disasters, public health, and social security. Through the visual monitoring mechanism of Big Data, managers can be assisted in early warning, command, and dispatch during the event, analysis, and judgment after the event so as to improve the efficiency of emergency command and dispatch of traffic management departments.

4.4.3 *Transportation simulation*

The urban traffic Big Data system is undergoing complete reconstruction and the fusion analysis of Big Data provides the possibility for multidimensional smart traffic analysis. The advent of the 5G era will endow traffic Big Data with two characteristics: The first one is that massive data will bring opportunities and challenges. Analyzing massive data requires the support of the transportation industry and the accumulation of transportation majors. The other one is fragmentation. Integration of traditional data with new data, historical data, and real-time data is the largest challenge to traffic Big Data.

A closed-loop system of data collection, fusion, calculation, application, and feedback in the established Dynamic origin–destination (OD) estimation is regarded as the core technology. The impact of various traffic plans on traffic flow can be simulated and evaluated in real time. The preview of various preset schemes under complex traffic conditions can be carried out and the optimal traffic improvement or management scheme can be quickly and effectively selected. It is not only developing toward urban traffic control but also toward future autonomous driving and future mobility as a service (MaaS) development.

4.4.3.1 *Monitoring of passenger flow diversion in the station*

5G and edge computing technology combined with station video data can be applied to monitor the passenger flow and the changing trend of traffic stations. Three kinds of bearing states can be set based on the passenger flow carrying capacity: comfortable, moderate, and crowded. When the passenger flow is in a crowded state, early warning will be set and emergency plans will begin. The on-site surveillance video can be used to view the on-site images. The security personnel configuration can be added based on the need to maintain the on-site order and provide manual guidance or mobilize taxis to evacuate the passenger flow. At the same time, evacuation and appeasement information can be accurately sent to the people inside this area, persuading people to remain there to ease the congestion of passenger flow.

4.4.3.2 *Passenger flow forecasting and security deployment*

(1) *Forecast and guarantee of station passenger flow*: The scale of passenger flow in major holidays and the gathering of passenger flow at different times can be predicted based on the historical passenger flow data of transportation stations on different dates. It can provide a reference for station management to formulate the holiday protection plan in advance and good deployment of security personnel at entrance and exit gates. Based on the forecast of passenger flow entering and leaving the station, the number of gates opening and departures as well as the frequency of departures at different times can be deployed.

(2) *Forecast and guarantee of passenger flow in water transportation*: A model can be established based on the conditions of the channel segment, the location and quantity of anchorages, and the total number of anchors. The relevant dispatching or ship organization rules can be introduced combined with the historical data of the water transport hub to simulate and reproduce the water transport traffic flow, thus predicting the water transport passenger flow. The flow early warning

and control can be realized to avoid the traffic bottleneck or serious blockage, improving the regional capacity and management level of the water transport hub.

(3) *Forecast and guarantee of airport passenger flow*: The traffic flow of private cars, taxis, trucks, and buses entering the airport terminal around the airport is simulated. The traffic flow information of the road network around the airport and the traffic flow information entering the airport parking lot are obtained through simulation. It can also simulate the passenger flow in the airport and predict the passenger flow distribution in the future or in a certain period of time by combining with the historical data. Therefore, a good allocation of personnel and resources will be made in advance and the orderly operation of the airport is ensured.

(4) *Passenger flow simulation of urban rail transit stations*: Based on the streamline behavior of passenger flow in the normal state of rail transit and the emergency evacuation design of passenger flow under abnormal conditions, the simulation model of passenger flow in stations can be constructed with the space and time characteristics of rail transit flow as well as the characteristics of the passengers' individual travel. Through the simulation analysis of station passenger flow, the passenger flow of rail transit and stations can be estimated. Meanwhile, congestion can be predicted to provide the decision-making reference for passenger transportation organization and passenger flow control.

(5) *Emergency evacuation simulation*: The simulation model of passenger flow emergency evacuation can be established to simulate station passenger flow evacuation under different emergency evacuation strategies and visually show the evacuation effects of different modes. It is helpful to formulate an effective emergency evacuation plan to reduce the operational losses caused by emergencies.

With 5G, Big Data, cloud services, and artificial intelligence constituting the technical cornerstones of the new generation smart transportation system, the traditional transportation system is undergoing changes. With the gradual integration of 5G and artificial intelligence into smart transportation systems, safety, reliability, and operational efficiency of transportation systems are constantly improving. With the help of the new generation communication network and data processing capability, the operational efficiency of the whole smart transportation system is continuously improving. The energy loss is continuously lowered, and the whole transportation process becomes safer and more convenient.

In the 5G era, the main development trends of smart transportation are as follows:

(1) *Traffic emergency linkage and safety guarantee in active mode*: The smart driving information service platform app can be developed based on the traffic information collection system. Real-time traffic flow, average speed of traffic flow, congestion status, and destination parking lot resources can be sent to the users' mobile phone terminals and on-board interconnection system terminals by the system. Users can view real-time monitoring images and master first-hand information in the car by use of the ultra-fast data transmission rate of 5G based on their needs.

(2) *Comprehensive traffic intelligent service system based on mobile Internet*: The electronic toll collection (ETC) system based on the Internet of Things can be constructed with technical means such as vehicle identification, truck weighing, route identification, and mobile payment to realize free-flow toll collection. A vehicle–road collaborative service system based on the Internet of Vehicles can be created to provide traffic information for road users. 5G mobile operators provide specific base stations, ensuring safe travel of the public.

(3) *Accurate perception and intelligent control system in traffic operation state*: Multi-source data collection can be made possible through vehicle identification, geomagnetic induction, high-definition monitoring, and meteorological monitoring. Abnormal road traffic events such as congestion, illegal stop, rain, and fog and fire accidents can be dynamically monitored. Video analysis technology provides a base for implementing early warning of traffic conditions and guides vehicles to change lanes or choose routes in advance. Such information can also be sent to the local taxi command system, making the taxi running more efficient.

(4) *Intelligent vehicles and collaborative control between people and vehicles*: The running status of vehicles can be monitored in real time through vehicle identification equipment, vehicle-mounted positioning

system, and vehicle over temperature detection system. Regular warnings will be issued to drivers of passenger and freight vehicles, such as prohibiting fatigue driving and forcing vehicle cooling. Smart vehicles equipped with various sensors can scan roadside parking spaces and transmit the data to the cloud. Then, the data will be distributed to all cars, helping to solve the parking problem. Vehicles equipped with smart cameras can collect key information such as lane lines and road signs in daily driving to generate high-precision maps. With this set of maps, unmanned vehicles can obtain external road condition in real time or self-position based on high-precision maps transmitted from the background, thus speeding up the process of mass production of unmanned vehicles.

Bibliography

AI Transportation (November 2, 2018, April 20, 2020). Top-level design of intelligent transportation management. https://www.sohu.com/a/272714219_468661.

Automobile Market (December 24, 2018, April 20, 2020). 5G is coming with so many connections to cars. https://www.sohu.com/a/284117168_115542.

Bao Cheng (2017). Multi-lane ETC system realization based on MIMO-employed technology. *Fujian Computer* (9): 155, 161–162.

Cai Wenhai (2018). *Intelligent Transportation Practice*. Beijing: Posts & Telecom Press.

Chen Caijun, Liu Zhan, Qian Xiaohong *et al.* (2015). *Intelligent Transportation*. Beijing: Tsinghua University Press.

Chen Hourun (November 6, 2018, April 20, 2020). 2020 Key global countries intelligent transportation industry development plans summary. https://www.qianzhan.com/analyst/detail/220/181105-b6fa5522.html.

Chen Jianeng and Li Dan (2019). Analysis of the future development of the shared car industry. *Cooperative Economy and Science* (24): 34–35.

Chen Ming, Miu Qingyu, and Liu Yin (2017). *5G Mobile Wireless Communication Technology*. Beijing: Posts & Telecom Press.

Chen Yan and Chen Hao (2014). Intelligent transportation enlightenment from Japan. *China Economic Herald*, 05–13 (A04).

China Academy of Information and Communications Technology (November 4, 2019, April 20, 2020). The "White Paper on Vehicle High-precision Positioning" released by IMT-2020 (5G) Promotion Group. https://mp.weixin.qq.com/s/1Fl_VEN0kNsnFePRybEovg.

China's Communist Party Central Committee, the State Council (September 19, 2019, April 20, 2020). Outline of building a powerful transportation country. http://www.gov.cn/zhengce/2019-09/19/content_5431432.htm.

Fangcun Technology (December 16, 2019, April 20, 2020). What is "non-sensing payment?" Don't be misled. https://m.sohu.com/a/233603553_100151036.

Global Car (December 6, 2019, April 20, 2020). Open the 5G era, the ultimate solution for L5 autonomous driving released by the Chinese team. https://new.qq.com/omn/20190121/20190121A17VWT.html.

HeiKe (March 21, 2017, April 20, 2020). Establishment of US intelligent transportation research and test smart center to help future automobile development. https://www.sohu.com/a/129571915_455835.

Hua Pan (December 15, 2018, April 20, 2020). Shared vehicles vision with Internet+5G+AI. https://baijiahao.baidu.com/s?id=1619926009128605798&wfr=spider&for=pc.

HuaZai (August 10, 2016, April 20, 2020). The evolution history of in-vehicle entertainment equipment. https://tech.hqew.com/fangan_124325.

IMT-2020 (5G) Promotion Group (June 24, 2014, April 20, 2020). White paper on 5G vision and demand. https://wenku.baidu.com/view/725a6c74a5e9856a561260bd.html.

International Car Rental (June 13, 2019, April 20, 2020). Automobile industry competition in the 5G era has started with the shared car being the main battlefield? https://www.sohu.com/a/320157615_194241.

IXDC (June 26, 2019, April 2, 2020). The trend, four major designs of the future car entertainment system. https://www.sohu.com/a/323151692_207454.

Jin Huiqing, Dai Ping, and Zhang Shulin (2001). Current research and future expectation of the intelligent transportation system (ITS). *Ergonomics* 7(3): 39–41.

Liang Wei and Yuan Shuai (April 11, 2019, April 20, 2020). What changes will 5G bring to the transportation?. https://www.sohu.com/a/307246261_100122961.

Lian Limin (July 3, 2019, April 20, 2020). Baidu Maps Li Ying: Smarter travel planning is the future trend. https://tech.huanqiu.com/article/9CaKrnKlj1L.

Liao Hongwei (2004). *Thinking of the Chinese Intelligent Transportation Development*. Chengdu: Southwest Jiaotong University.

Li Chuanpeng and Wang Xiuxu (2019). MaaS reference of foreign development experience — Take the Finnish Whim application as an example. China Information Technology (10): 46–47.

lihao1987617, (December 31, 2019, April 20, 2020). Central control for the traffic signal control system solution. https://wenku.baidu.com/view/350dee71c8aedd3383c4bb4cf7ec4afe04a1b1ce.html.

Li Rui, Li Wei, and Wu Yong (2011). Introduction to Japan's intelligent transportation system and its references. *China ITS Journal* (1): 123–126.

Liu Da (August 28, 2019, April 20, 2020). What changes and reforms will 5G bring to the car industry?. https://www.zhihu.com/question/328682155.

Liu Kuang (May 4, 2017, April 20, 2020). Car sharing started in Europe and America but is destined to rise in China?. https://www.d1ev.com/kol/51642.

Liu Yuncai, Zhang Su, and Shi Pengfei (2011). Overview of the international development of intelligent transportation and domestic priority issues. *Highway* (11): 26–34.

Li Xinjia (2004). European intelligent transportation construction situation and enlightenment. *Urban Transport* (2): 58–62.

Li Yan (2019). *5G and Internet of Vehicles, Internet of Vehicles Technology and Intelligent Connected Cars Based on Mobile Communication.* Beijing: Publishing House of Electronics Industry.

Li Ye, Wang Mi, and Shu Hanyu (2018). Mobility-as-a-Service (MaaS) systematic analysis reviews. *China Transportation Review* 40(9): 56–65.

Li Zhaorong (2016). *Crossover Growth with the Evolution of IOV*. Beijing: Publishing House of Electronics Industry.

Lu Huapu and Li Ruimin (2014). The development status and trend of urban intelligent transportation system. *Journal of Engineering Studies* 6(1): 6–19.

Nanchang Liuhuan Technology (June 27, 2019, April 20, 2020). What are the differences between non-sensing payment and ETC? Who will be the mainstream?. https://www.sohu.com/a/323343282_120122137.

Peng Qi (January 15, 2020, April 20, 2020). Don't be overlooked. Where are ETC's advantages and future?. http://www.cnsoftnews.com/news/202001/80237.html.

People's Daily Online Popular Science (September 11, 2019, April 20, 2020). Do you know the principle of High Speed ETC's fast passage?. https://www.sohu.com/a/340216044_120045299.

Prime Technology (October 25, 2019, April 20, 2020). Understand how new technologies, car payment, 3D behavior analysis, etc. empower intelligent transportation. https://www.sohu.com/a/349460953_354564.

Qi Shirong (2016). *Chinese History (Volume 2, Grade 7)*. Beijing: People's Education Press.

Qu Dayi, Chen Xiufeng, Wei Jinli et al. (2017). *Intelligent Transportation System and Its Technical Applications*. Release 2. Beijing: China Machine Press.

Ren Yan (January 10, 2020, April 20, 2020). First online "Spring Festival Traffic Forecast" system released by Amap today in China. http://www.chinahighway.com/article/65381261.html.

Research Institute of Curriculum and Textbooks, People's Education Press, Research and Development Center for History Curriculum and Textbooks (2019). *Normal High School Curriculum Standard Experimental Textbook Compulsory History 2*. Beijing: People's Education Press.

Research Institute of Curriculum and Textbooks, Research and Development Center for History and Society Curriculum Textbooks (2018). *Compulsory Education Textbook History and Society Grade 8 Volume 2*. Beijing: People's Education Press.

Tang Cheng (March 3, 2019, April 20, 2020). Where will the traditional ETC go in the 5G era?. https://www.iyiou.com/p/93866.html.

The Ministry of Transport (April 12, 2019, April 20, 2020). 2018 Statistical bulletin on the development of the transportation industry. http://xxgk.mot.gov.cn/jigou/zhghs/201904/t20190412_3186720.html.

The Ministry of Transport (July 25, 2019, April 20, 2020). Notice of the Ministry of Communications on Issuing the "Outline of Digital Transportation Development Plan". http://xxgk.mot.gov.cn/jigou/zhghs/201907/t20190725_3230528.html.

The Ministry of Transport (December 12, 2019, April 20, 2020). Notice of the Ministry of Transport on Issuing the Action Plan for Promoting the Development of Comprehensive Transportation Big Data (2020–2025). http://xxgk.mot.gov.cn/jigou/kjs/201912/t20191212_3308474.html.

The State Council (March 1, 2017, April 20, 2020). Notice of the State Council on Issuing the Development Plan of the "13th Five-Year" Modern Comprehensive Transportation System. http://xxgk.mot.gov.cn/jigou/zhghs/201703/t20170301_2976485.html.

Wang Dongzhu and Yang Qi (2013). Analysis of the development status and related standards of European cooperative intelligent transportation systems. *Journal of Highway and Transportation Research and Development* 30(9): 128–133.

Wang Guoping (2010). *What to do with the City?*. Beijing: People's Publishing House.

Wang Jian (2018). What is Mobility-as-a-Service (MaaS)?. *People's Public Transportation* (5): 34–36.

Wang Quan (2018). *From Internet of Vehicles to Autonomous Driving*. Beijing: Posts & Telecom Press.

Wang Yanchen (2016). *Intelligent Factory, the Trend of Intelligent Manufacturing in China*. Beijing: China Industry and Commerce Associated Press.

Wanzhuanhezi (August 2, 2019, April 20, 2020). Working principle and advantages of highway ETC. https://baijiahao.baidu.com/s?id=1640747906901161084&wfr=spider&for=pc.

Wu Shuanshuan (February 15, 2015, April 20, 2020). Device-to-Device (D2D) applications in 5G. https://www.zte.com.cn/china/about/magazine/zte-technologies/2015/2/cn_1193/431612.

www.zol.com. (July 28, 2019, April 20, 2020). 5G will solve the biggest pain point of mobile navigation and high-precision positioning will become the standard. https://baijiahao.baidu.com/s?id=1640263778380397412&wfr=spider&for=pc.

Xiang Ligang (2019). *5G Era: What is 5G and How will it Change the World?*. Beijing: China Renmin University Press.
Xiao Huoche and Hao Duoyu (2016). *The Myth of 5G*. Publishing House of Electronics Industry of China.
Xu Huafeng, Xia Chuang, and Sun Lin (2013). Intelligent transportation system (ITS) and applications in Japan. *Highway* (9): 187–191.
Xu Xiaoqi (2015). *Internet of Vehicles*. Beijing: Chemical Industry Press.
Xu Yong (2016). Thinking of studies on intelligent transportation system (ITS) in US. *Qinghai Transportation Science and Technology* (2): 13–15, 31.
Yi Hanwen (2002). American intelligent transportation 10-year development plan. *Urban Planning International* (04): 40–44.
Zhu Donghui (2002). Intelligent transportation system (ITS) development. *Journal of Shandong Jiaotong University* 10(4): 9–14.

Index

5G, v–vii, ix–xi, xiii–xv, 12, 25, 27, 31–33, 35–39, 41, 45–50, 54, 57–59, 61–63, 65, 68–70, 73–75, 77, 82, 84, 86–87, 89–94, 98, 101–111, 112–115, 118–122
5G intelligent lane control, 94–96
13th five-year plan, 20, 22–23

A
action outline for promoting the development of Big Data, the, 20, 22
adaptive traffic light control, 93–94
Advanced Driver Assistant System (ADAS), 9
ancient transportation, 2–6
AR glasses handling emergencies, 102

B
bus route optimization, 99

C
changes in car sharing caused by 5G, 82
C-V2X, 35, 45–48, 54

D
development of intelligent transportation, the, 15–20
Development Plan for Digital Transport, 20, 23–24

E
edge of computing, 34–35
end-to-end (D2D) communication technology, 41–44

H
high-precision positioning, 44–46, 54, 63, 68, 102

I
Intelligent Transportation, 12–13
Internet of Vehicles, the, 18, 34–35, 43–44, 46–48, 54, 122

L
large-scale multi-input multi-output, 38–39
latter-day transportation, 6–8

M
modern transportation, 8–12

N
network slicing, 39, 42, 54
nine key capabilities of 5G, 32

O
"one information-integrated map" of intelligent transportation, 90

P
program of building national strength in transportation, 20–21

R
red light interception of vehicles violating traffic rules, 97

S
Smart City, ix, 14, 16, 27, 29
Spring Festival transportation forecasting system, 64

T
to prevent traffic accidents, 116
top-level design of intelligent transportation, the, 51

traffic Big Data acquisition and data center, 52
traffic Big Data business application platform, 52
traffic Big Data command and decision visualization platform, 52, 54–55
traffic Big Data sharing and analysis platform, 52,
transportation policies, 25
travel planning in the 5G era, 61

U
ultra-dense networking, 35–37, 54
Urbanization development, 12–13

W
walking around the airport only with customer's face, 110